Learning to Compute

FOURTH EDITION

Harcourt Brace Jovanovich

New York   Chicago   San Francisco   Atlanta   Dallas   *and*   London

Editorial Advisors

The contributions of John R. Clark, Mary A. Potter, and Wilmer L. Jones to earlier editions of *Learning to Compute* are gratefully acknowledged.

Printed in the United States of America

ISBN 0-15-357763-0

Contents

Addition with Whole Numbers

1. Survey Test

▶ Add.

	a	b	c	d	e	f	g	h	i
1.	5 8	7 6	9 5	8 6	3 9	7 9	9 9	4 8	6 5

	a	b	c	d	e	f	g	h	i
2.	8 8 7	9 7 6	3 9 8	5 7 9	7 9 7	8 26	37 9	26 48	72 93

	a	b	c	d	e	f	g	h	i
3.	7 9 5 8 6	3 9 4 8 7	13 66 27 45 18	50 38 76 25 49	378 782 926 247	2792 876 465 1728	9762 487 826 4728 986	827 976 2862 496 9976	9874 7208 9414 8625 1775

2. Inventory Test

Basic Addition Facts

▶ Add.

	a	b	c	d	e	f	g	h	i	j	k
1.	4 9	1 7	6 1	9 1	5 5	7 2	6 8	8 7	2 6	9 5	8 6
2.	8 1	5 3	6 6	5 9	3 5	4 4	8 2	3 3	5 4	7 3	1 8
3.	1 9	2 7	9 6	2 8	1 4	8 8	9 2	9 7	1 6	9 9	6 2
4.	3 8	7 6	9 3	7 8	3 6	8 5	7 9	5 7	1 5	3 9	4 5
5.	5 8	3 7	6 5	9 8	4 7	3 1	0 7	6 7	8 9	6 3	4 8
6.	5 6	6 0	6 9	8 3	4 6	5 2	9 4	7 5	7 7	2 9	8 4

ORDER IN ADDITION

The order in which you add two numbers <u>does not change the sum.</u>

Example:
$8 + 7 = 15$
$7 + 8 = 15$
$\mathbf{8 + 7 = 7 + 8}$

$$8 \longleftarrow \text{Addend} \longrightarrow 7$$
$$\underline{+7} \longleftarrow \text{Addend} \longrightarrow \underline{+8}$$
$$15 \longleftarrow \text{Sum} \longrightarrow 15$$

Remember that the sum of a number and zero is the number.

Example: $0 + 6 = 6$ and $6 + 0 = 6$

2A. Practice Set

▶ Add.

	a	b	c	d	e	f	g	h	i	j	k
1.	4 3	3 4	4 9	4 5	8 7	7 8	1 2	8 8	6 1	7 7	9 1
2.	6 8	8 6	8 1	4 8	3 3	3 7	8 9	8 5	1 3	2 7	5 9
3.	7 4	4 6	1 9	6 4	2 3	7 6	0 9	3 1	6 6	8 2	2 8
4.	9 2	4 7	3 8	4 2	5 7	0 7	6 3	5 2	2 6	4 1	3 2
5.	7 9	3 6	2 4	2 9	6 7	5 3	3 9	2 5	6 0	1 5	7 5
6.	7 2	1 4	5 6	1 1	2 2	1 7	9 9	9 7	6 5	1 6	8 3
7.	9 4	3 5	5 8	1 8	0 6	7 1	7 3	0 8	9 3	5 4	9 8
8.	5 1	9 5	8 4	6 9	0 4	5 5	9 0	2 1	4 4	7 0	9 6

GROUPING IN ADDITION

When you find the sum of three numbers, it does not matter which two numbers you add first.

Sometimes it is helpful to look for two numbers whose sum is 10.

Examples:

a.
$$\begin{array}{r} 7 \\ 3 \\ +9 \\ \hline 19 \end{array} \; 10 \quad \text{or} \quad \begin{array}{r} 7 \\ 3 \\ +9 \\ \hline 19 \end{array} \; 12$$

b.
$$\begin{array}{r} 4 \\ 8 \\ +6 \\ \hline 18 \end{array} \; 10 \quad \text{or} \quad \begin{array}{r} 4 \\ 8 \\ +6 \\ \hline 18 \end{array} \; 12$$

3. Inventory Test

▶ Add in the order that is easiest for you.

	a	b	c	d	e	f	g	h	i	j
1.	4 6 2	5 8 2	7 2 3	8 1 9	2 3 8	3 7 6	4 8 7	6 9 3	9 7 4	1 6 7
2.	7 6 5	9 2 6	5 7 5	2 8 6	6 6 5	7 2 4	4 6 7	5 9 5	4 8 3	9 9 6
3.	6 7 8	2 9 3	8 9 8	9 9 9	2 7 5	9 3 9	3 7 8	9 2 9	2 5 8	7 7 7

3A. Practice Set

▶ Add.

	a	b	c	d	e	f	g	h	i	j
1.	8 6 4	7 5 3	5 5 6	4 2 6	7 7 8	5 9 1	2 4 9	5 5 5	9 8 1	6 6 6
2.	4 4 9	2 7 3	4 9 6	8 8 6	7 5 8	8 2 6	3 8 7	2 5 9	4 7 6	8 1 8
3.	7 4 7	9 4 6	3 8 8	9 5 9	2 7 7	8 8 8	6 7 4	5 8 7	6 9 6	2 6 8

HORIZONTAL ADDITION

Sometimes it is convenient to add horizontally. Group in the way that is easiest for you.

Examples: a. $9 + 8 + 1 = ?$ **b.** $6 + 6 + 8 + 4 = ?$

Solutions: a. $9 + 8 + 1 = 10 + 8$ **b.** $6 + 6 + 8 + 4 = 10 + 14$

$= 18$ $= 24$

4. Inventory Test

▶ Add.

	a	b	c
1.	$8 + 3 + 2 =$	$7 + 5 + 5 =$	$7 + 6 + 5 + 4 =$
2.	$6 + 5 + 4 =$	$9 + 2 + 7 =$	$9 + 4 + 7 + 3 =$
3.	$9 + 6 + 6 =$	$5 + 6 + 5 =$	$8 + 2 + 6 + 5 =$
4.	$7 + 2 + 2 =$	$4 + 2 + 7 =$	$4 + 9 + 7 + 8 =$
5.	$4 + 9 + 4 =$	$9 + 8 + 8 =$	$5 + 7 + 7 + 6 =$

4A. Practice Set

▶ Add.

	a	b	c
1.	$2 + 7 + 9 =$	$8 + 5 + 6 =$	$2 + 8 + 9 + 7 =$
2.	$4 + 7 + 8 =$	$7 + 7 + 9 =$	$7 + 4 + 7 + 4 =$
3.	$9 + 5 + 7 =$	$2 + 8 + 3 =$	$6 + 9 + 3 + 2 =$
4.	$2 + 4 + 9 =$	$9 + 4 + 9 =$	$8 + 7 + 6 + 3 =$
5.	$8 + 8 + 8 =$	$7 + 9 + 5 =$	$6 + 5 + 8 + 4 =$
6.	$6 + 7 + 3 =$	$3 + 7 + 6 =$	$9 + 4 + 4 + 8 =$

ADDING TWO-DIGIT NUMBERS

Example: $57 + 39 = ?$

Solution: Step 1: Add the ones.   **Step 2:** Add the tens.

$7 + 9 = 16$ $10 + 50 + 30 = 90$

$\begin{array}{r} 1 \\ 57 \\ +39 \\ \hline 6 \end{array}$ $\begin{array}{r} 1 \\ 57 \\ +39 \\ \hline 96 \end{array}$

5. Inventory Test

▶ Add.

	a	b	c	d	e	f	g	h	i
1.	15 14	23 18	24 16	37 22	36 26	42 17	69 23	45 27	28 83
2.	36 45	19 26	72 45	34 27	48 48	43 25	81 27	96 41	17 76

5A. Practice Set

▶ Add.

	a	b	c	d	e	f	g	h	i
1.	44 23	28 16	73 61	48 91	27 27	33 24	65 92	74 37	40 39
2.	37 23	76 45	21 33	46 22	97 21	28 43	42 54	37 18	72 29
3.	14 38	56 48	11 24	39 24	53 21	18 76	42 37	75 18	24 24
4.	35 62	17 85	46 43	81 29	56 39	38 58	61 14	74 37	49 63

6. Inventory Test

Several Addends

▶ Find these sums. Group in the easiest way for you.

	a	b	c	d	e	f	g	h	i	j
1.	8 7 2 5 4	7 6 3 8 4	5 7 6 2 5	4 7 8 2 9	6 8 4 3 1	5 9 2 7 3	4 4 7 6 3	9 1 2 7 6	2 7 6 3 5	4 1 7 9 8
2.	2 8 7 6 5 9	7 3 4 2 5 8	6 5 9 1 4 8	2 9 7 3 8 6	5 7 5 4 3 8	9 2 1 8 8 6	4 6 7 2 9 3	1 8 7 7 5 6	9 9 2 8 7 4	3 6 7 8 5 5

6A. Practice Set

▶Add. Group in the way that is easiest for you.

	a	b	c	d	e	f	g	h	i	j
1.	4	2	8	1	9	4	8	5	4	8
	6	7	4	7	8	4	9	5	8	4
	3	3	6	8	1	7	2	3	7	9
	9	9	7	7	3	3	7	8	5	3
	2	5	2	6	6	8	4	6	3	6
2.	4	2	4	9	7	4	7	5	1	8
	8	9	7	2	8	7	4	8	7	6
	2	5	8	1	6	3	9	3	3	8
	7	6	3	7	5	8	3	4	2	6
	3	1	2	3	4	2	6	4	9	7
	5	7	5	6	2	9	5	6	4	4

ADDITION—THREE-DIGIT NUMBERS

Example: $341 + 679 + 250 + 877 = ?$

Solution:

1: Add the ones

$1 + 9 + 0 + 7$
$= \mathbf{17}$

```
  1
 341
 679
 250
+877
   7
```

2: Add the tens.

$10 + 40 + 70 + 50$
$+ 70 = \mathbf{24}0$

```
 21
 341
 679
 250
+877
  47
```

3. Add the hundreds.

$200 + 300 + 600 + 200$
$+ 800 = \mathbf{21}00$

```
 21
 341
 679
 250
+877
2147
```

---

7. Inventory Test

▶Add.

	a	b	c	d	e	f	g
1.		43		72	45	66	273
	42	29	38	53	27	27	421
	37	81	63	28	91	57	826
	93	35	25	36	86	83	443
2.	65		442	472	402	986	421
	28	374	721	863	788	724	778
	76	265	180	109	634	225	482
	18	713	263	763	219	170	909

7A. Practice Set

▶ Add.

	a	b	c	d	e	f	g
1.	27 38 43 27	55 18 20 17	43 79 82 47	245 173 603 144	782 215 634 886	416 278 114 806	915 728 436 842
2.	638 421 752 803	411 278 315 676	420 555 738 932	561 207 119 486	328 217 846 103	777 582 460 285	143 821 786 945

8. Inventory Test
More Challenging Exercises

▶ Add.

	a	b	c	d	e	f
1.	274 4362 183 3074	6251 478 2114 768	932 78 2417 896	8641 782 905 1276	3636 825 741 9116	472 863 948 745
2.	7234 125 904 6112 733	605 1273 864 1437 786	4625 743 1276 881 408	1275 823 1176 863 92	1658 703 186 9125 825	4175 904 1263 818 4726

8A. Practice Set

▶ Add.

	a	b	c	d	e	f
1.	26 814 279 843	3474 47 483 343	9292 381 425 7114	5674 891 764 2073	3717 825 9163 704	632 4011 723 568
2.	2743 824 4343 712 406	4072 822 416 3365 46	5127 843 919 2736 464	3724 622 7403 382 444	5426 843 2761 104 85	226 1372 148 189 4278

▶ Add.

1. 8
4
9

2. 26
47

3. 86
24
73

4. 7
3
5
9

5. 862
78
453
115

6. 27 + 35 + 64 =

7. 276 + 36 + 475 =

8. 916
8432
745

9. 9706
824
7638
4711

10. Write the score for the winning basketball team.

Bullets	26	31	29	27
Royals	28	24	32	34

Stop! Try the Survey Test on page 1 again. See if you can make a perfect score.

Career Capsule

Bank tellers handle deposits and withdrawals. When accepting a deposit, the teller always checks the accuracy of the deposit slip.

In Exercises **1–12,** find the TOTAL on each deposit slip.

1.

		DOLLARS	CENTS
CASH		72	00
CHECKS	1	25	00
	2	63	00
	3		
TOTAL			

2.

		DOLLARS	CENTS
CASH		92	00
CHECKS	1	247	00
	2	35	00
	3		
TOTAL			

3.

		DOLLARS	CENTS
CASH		89	00
CHECKS	1	76	00
	2	48	00
	3	35	00
TOTAL			

4.

		DOLLARS	CENTS
CASH		198	00
CHECKS	1	154	00
	2	631	00
	3	480	00
TOTAL			

5.

		DOLLARS	CENTS
CASH		172	00
CHECKS	1	285	00
	2	398	00
	3	109	00
TOTAL			

6.

		DOLLARS	CENTS
CASH		270	00
CHECKS	1	988	00
	2	540	00
	3	832	00
TOTAL			

7.

		DOLLARS	CENTS
CASH		560	00
CHECKS	1	709	00
	2	653	00
	3	150	00
TOTAL			

8.

		DOLLARS	CENTS
CASH		202	00
CHECKS	1	185	00
	2	632	00
	3	109	00
TOTAL			

9.

		DOLLARS	CENTS
CASH		725	00
CHECKS	1	100	00
	2	409	00
	3	832	00
TOTAL			

10.

		DOLLARS	CENTS
CASH		490	00
CHECKS	1	681	00
	2	540	00
	3	978	00
TOTAL			

11.

		DOLLARS	CENTS
CASH		625	00
CHECKS	1	25	00
	2	189	00
	3	54	00
TOTAL			

12.

		DOLLARS	CENTS
CASH		348	00
CHECKS	1	159	00
	2	487	00
	3	86	00
TOTAL			

APPLICATIONS

Transportation

▶ This table gives the base price of three types of cars and the cost of optional equipment. Use the table for Exercises **1–6**.

| Type of Car | Base Price | Optional Equipment | | | | |
		Automatic Transmission	Power Steering	Power Brakes	AM Radio	Air Conditioning
Compact	$4623	$262	$136	$57	$68	$452
Intermediate	$5106	$274	$136	$62	$74	$484
Standard	$3898	—	—	—	$68	$502

1. What is the base price of a standard car?

2. What is the cost of a standard car with all five options?

3. What is the cost of an intermediate car?

4. What is the cost of a compact car with AM radio and power brakes?

5. What is the cost of an intermediate car with all five options?

6. What is the cost of a compact car with all five options?

Housing

7. The Simpsons pay $168 a month for mortgage, taxes, and insurance. They also pay $87 per month for utilities. Find the total of these expenses.

8. Each month the Fannelli family pays $196 for the mortgage, $140 for taxes, $45 for utilities, and $60 for fuel oil. Find the total of these expenses.

Measurement

The distance around a figure is its **perimeter.** To find the perimeter of each figure in Exercises **9–12,** add the lengths of its sides.

▶ Find the perimeter.

Example:

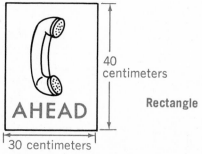

40 centimeters

Rectangle

30 centimeters

AHEAD

Solution: Perimeter = 40 + 30 + 40 + 30
Perimeter = **140 centimeters**

Note that the shape of the sign at the left is a **rectangle.** In a rectangle, opposite sides have the same length.

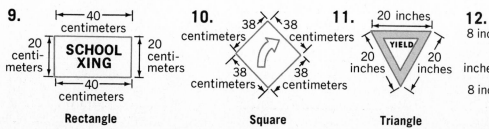

9.
40 centimeters
20 centimeters
SCHOOL XING
20 centimeters
40 centimeters
Rectangle

10.
38 centimeters
38 centimeters
38 centimeters
38 centimeters
Square

11.
20 inches
20 inches
20 inches
YIELD
Triangle

12.
8 inches
8 inches
8 inches
8 inches
8 inches
8 inches
8 inches
8 inches
STOP
Octagon

Multiplication with Whole Numbers

9. Survey Test

▶ Multiply.

	a	b	c	d	e	f	g	h
1.	7 0	6 5	9 3	8 9	6 7	7 8	6 4	9 9
2.	47 3	86 7	72 5	70 9	312 6	478 9	279 8	404 6
3.	46 24	35 50	76 48	43 87	268 28	709 34	795 346	128 207

RELATING ADDITION AND MULTIPLICATION

ADDITION

8
8
8
8
8
8
+8
——
48

Six 8's

MULTIPLICATION

You can find the sum of six 8's by multiplying 8 and 6.

$$6 \times 8 = \mathbf{48}$$

$$8 + 8 + 8 + 8 + 8 + 8 = 6 \times 8 = \mathbf{48}$$

---

10. Inventory Test

Basic Multiplication Facts

▶ Multiply.

	a	b	c	d	e	f	g	h	i	j
1.	3 3	7 8	1 9	4 4	2 7	5 6	3 6	5 7	1 3	2 4
2.	1 4	9 8	5 5	0 5	6 7	7 7	2 5	8 5	6 6	3 8
3.	2 2	4 7	3 4	4 5	1 7	8 7	2 8	8 2	4 8	1 6
4.	2 6	7 9	9 7	8 9	3 7	5 8	2 3	6 8	4 9	3 9

10

ORDER IN MULTIPLICATION

The order in which you multiply two numbers <u>does not change the</u> <u>product.</u>

Example: $7 \times 4 = 28$
$4 \times 7 = 28$
$7 \times 4 = 4 \times 7$

7	←——Factors——→	4
×4	←——Factors——→	×7
28	←——Product——→	28

Remember that the product of a number and zero is zero.

Example: $0 \times 6 = 0$ and $6 \times 0 = 0$

10A. Practice Set

▶Multiply.

	a	b	c	d	e	f	g	h	i	j
1.	3 9	6 2	2 6	9 3	6 1	4 7	7 4	7 2	1 2	9 1
2.	2 3	1 0	5 3	4 5	1 9	1 1	3 7	2 4	4 4	1 5
3.	2 9	3 6	4 8	8 4	5 5	3 3	1 8	5 8	3 5	8 3
4.	8 1	3 4	6 7	3 1	7 9	4 6	9 9	0 1	8 5	6 9
5.	1 6	5 4	7 3	3 2	4 3	7 1	2 8	3 8	2 5	8 8
6.	9 2	4 9	9 4	2 7	5 9	6 8	5 6	9 7	7 8	7 7
7.	4 2	7 5	5 7	6 5	1 3	6 4	8 2	5 2	6 3	4 1
8.	5 1	8 6	9 8	9 5	9 9	7 6	9 6	8 9	8 7	6 6

11

METHODS OF MULTIPLYING

Here are two ways to find the product of 8 and 74.

Example: $8 \times 74 = ?$

Solutions: **One Method**   **Short Method**

```
                                          3
        74                                74
      × 8                               × 8
      ─────                             ─────
       32  ◄──────  8 × 4                592
      560  ◄──────  8 × 70
      ─────
      592  ◄──────  32 + 560
```

11. Inventory Test

▶ Multiply.

	a	b	c	d	e	f	g	h
1.	34 5	17 6	24 3	18 6	28 3	18 7	39 6	72 4
2.	83 7	36 6	45 6	57 8	113 6	78 6	44 9	214 7
3.	64 8	362 2	41 9	77 5	65 9	213 9	312 7	476 8

11A. Practice Set

▶ Find these products.

	a	b	c	d	e	f	g	h
1.	27 5	32 3	48 4	92 9	18 8	23 9	81 9	76 3
2.	223 7	85 6	56 7	94 7	263 5	218 4	75 9	172 6
3.	53 7	275 5	176 4	203 7	98 6	713 4	65 8	42 6
4.	69 6	417 4	812 5	29 7	43 8	233 6	702 4	129 8

GROUPING IN MULTIPLICATION

When you find the product of three numbers, it does not matter which two numbers you multiply first.

Examples: a. $4 \times 7 \times 3 = ?$ **b.** $5 \times 6 \times 3 = ?$

Solutions: a. $4 \times 7 \times 3 = \underline{4 \times 7} \times 3$ **b.** $5 \times 6 \times 3 = \underline{5 \times 6} \times 3$

$\qquad\qquad\quad = \quad 28 \quad \times 3 \qquad\qquad\qquad\qquad = \quad 30 \quad \times 3$

$\qquad\qquad\quad = 84 \qquad\qquad\qquad\qquad\qquad\qquad = 90$

OR   OR

$4 \times 7 \times 3 = 4 \times \underline{7 \times 3} \qquad\qquad 5 \times 6 \times 3 = 5 \times \underline{6 \times 3}$

$\qquad\qquad\quad = 4 \times \quad 21 \qquad\qquad\qquad\qquad = 5 \times \quad 18$

$\qquad\qquad\quad = 84 \qquad\qquad\qquad\qquad\qquad\qquad = 90$

12. Inventory Test

▶ Multiply. Group in the way that is easiest for you.

	a	b	c
1.	$2 \times 3 \times 4 =$	$3 \times 6 \times 2 =$	$7 \times 4 \times 3 =$
2.	$3 \times 4 \times 3 =$	$6 \times 5 \times 6 =$	$5 \times 6 \times 4 =$
3.	$3 \times 4 \times 5 =$	$4 \times 2 \times 5 =$	$8 \times 3 \times 2 =$
4.	$2 \times 4 \times 6 =$	$6 \times 3 \times 2 =$	$2 \times 9 \times 4 =$
5.	$4 \times 5 \times 3 =$	$3 \times 6 \times 3 =$	$5 \times 7 \times 6 =$

12A. Practice Set

▶ Find these products. Group in the way that is easiest for you.

	a	b	c
1.	$4 \times 2 \times 6 =$	$2 \times 5 \times 7 =$	$2 \times 9 \times 5 =$
2.	$9 \times 8 \times 5 =$	$8 \times 3 \times 5 =$	$7 \times 8 \times 3 =$
3.	$3 \times 8 \times 2 =$	$4 \times 2 \times 9 =$	$4 \times 6 \times 7 =$
4.	$9 \times 3 \times 4 =$	$5 \times 4 \times 3 =$	$2 \times 4 \times 9 =$
5.	$7 \times 6 \times 9 =$	$7 \times 7 \times 3 =$	$3 \times 6 \times 6 =$
6.	$5 \times 4 \times 7 =$	$4 \times 8 \times 6 =$	$8 \times 4 \times 6 =$

PARTIAL PRODUCTS IN MULTIPLICATION

In some multiplication problems, you have to write partial products.

Examples: a. $37 \times 56 = ?$ **b.** $423 \times 276 = ?$

Solutions: a.

```
              56
            × 37
Partial    ─────
Products    392  ◄──── 7 × 56
           1680  ◄──── 30 × 56
           ─────
           2072
```

b.

```
                276
              × 423
Partial      ──────
Products        828  ◄──── 3 × 276
               5520  ◄──── 20 × 276
             110400  ◄──── 400 × 276
             ───────
             116,748
```

13. Inventory Test

▶Multiply.

	a	b	c	d	e	f	g	h
1.	23 15	16 24	28 34	29 14	62 21	45 18	17 26	43 28
2.	26 73	91 26	47 25	23 19	46 36	66 24	26 39	60 23
3.	38 26	51 99	72 57	43 78	20 76	18 96	75 83	96 96

13A. Practice Set

▶Multiply.

	a	b	c	d	e	f	g	h
1.	24 32	75 49	36 18	21 49	98 36	34 25	72 20	45 48
2.	63 27	92 47	83 95	49 86	46 35	47 29	22 74	15 73
3.	80 76	88 37	43 71	83 92	58 69	69 58	24 72	55 64

14. Inventory Test

Avoiding Errors Caused by Zeros

▶ Multiply.

	a	b	c	d	e	f	g
1.	42 20	70 26	206 3	104 7	906 8	70 30	705 8
2.	305 18	610 15	208 24	37 30	409 46	206 96	100 28
3.	26 100	48 102	59 302	410 30	706 40	46 803	500 200

14A. Practice Set

▶ Multiply.

	a	b	c	d	e	f	g
1.	86 30	40 38	105 7	208 9	306 8	820 13	410 10
2.	506 32	740 38	203 14	100 26	230 39	405 20	606 38
3.	190 27	206 48	460 80	215 10	48 208	76 310	176 304

15. Inventory Test

More Challenging Exercises

▶ Multiply.

	a	b	c	d	e	f	g
1.	48 27	283 45	704 26	480 100	615 73	268 9	920 70
2.	2763 48	2473 103	976 96	430 540	476 38	4702 208	376 59

15A. Practice Set

▶ Multiply.

	a	b	c	d	e	f	g
1.	99 51	77 54	630 45	720 39	38 36	67 58	268 26
2.	5306 52	24 356	6157 38	7006 48	8274 94	514 200	824 742

► Find the answers.

1.	2.	3.	4.	5.
7 6 8 4 +9	87 46 28 92 +40	806 92 7649 + 876	762 × 9	902 × 10

6.	7.	8.	9.
400 ×300	98 ×78	895 ×65	87 ×274

10. At Herring Run Junior High there are 27 classes with 25 pupils, 18 classes with 28 pupils, and 26 classes with 32 pupils. What is the total enrollment?

Stop! Try the Survey Test on page 10 again. See if you can make a perfect score.

Career Capsule

Painters must be able to calculate the **surface area** of a room in order to find out how much paint is needed. The **surface area** of a room is the sum of the areas of its six surfaces.

► In Exercises **1–4,** find the surface area.

Example:

Solution:

	Length × Width =	Area
Area of floor:	8 × 10 =	80 square meters
Area of ceiling:	8 × 10 =	80 square meters
Area of right wall:	10 × 3 =	30 square meters
Area of left wall:	10 × 3 =	30 square meters
Area of front wall:	8 × 3 =	24 square meters
Area of back wall:	8 × 3 =	+24 square meters
	Surface area:	**268 square meters**

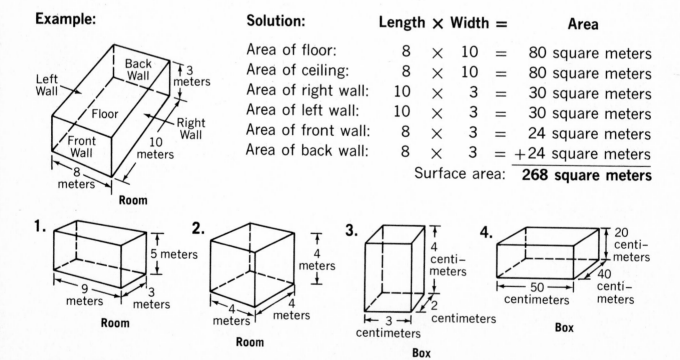

5. A painter has been hired to paint a room that is 11 meters long, 7 meters wide, and 3 meters high. She will <u>not</u> paint the floor. Find the total area of all the surfaces in the room to be painted.

APPLICATIONS

Food

1. Milo eats 3 slices of whole wheat bread each day. There are 55 calories in each slice.
How many calories are there in 3 slices?

2. Diana has 2 scrambled eggs for breakfast. Each scrambled egg contains 112 calories.
How many calories do 2 scrambled eggs contain?

3. Julia drinks 4 glasses of milk each day. There are 159 calories in one glass of milk.
How many calories are there in 4 glasses of milk?

4. Mr. Stanton is cooking 12 slices of bacon for his family. Each slice contains 48 calories.
How many calories do 12 slices of bacon contain?

Measurement

▶ In Exercises 5–8, find the area of the floor of each room.

Example: Bedroom
5 meters by 7 meters

Solution: Area = Length × Width
Area = 7 × 5 = **35 square meters**

5. Playroom: 7 meters by 3 meters

6. Kitchen: 3 meters by 4 meters

7. Bathroom: 2 meters by 3 meters

8. Living room: 5 meters by 6 meters

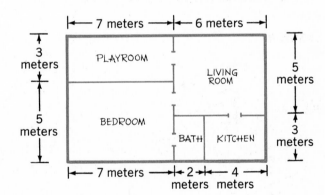

Statistics and Graphs

The bar graph at the right shows Dan Wilke's weekly income for the years 1978–1983.

9. In what year was Dan's weekly income the greatest?

10. In what year was Dan's weekly income the least?

11. In what year was Dan's weekly income about $360?

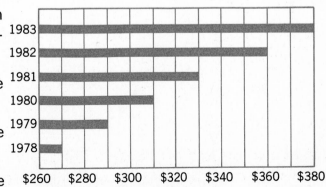

Weekly Income

Subtraction with Whole Numbers

16. Survey Test

▶ Subtract.

	a	b	c	d	e	f	g	h
1.	9 6	13 5	17 8	14 9	19 9	16 8	13 4	12 3
2.	37 8	26 9	75 8	63 21	83 65	82 49	98 89	70 26
3.	246 82	175 98	105 38	225 174	1635 872	200 76	8764 2985	4000 2176

RELATING ADDITION AND SUBTRACTION

Subtraction is the **opposite** operation of addition. Because of this, you can use addition to check subtraction.

Example: $73 - 21 = ?$ Check your answer.

Solution:
$$73$$
$$-21$$
$$\overline{52}$$

Check:
$$52$$
$$+21$$
$$\overline{73}$$

Same number

---

17. Inventory Test

Basic Subtraction Facts

▶ Subtract.

	a	b	c	d	e	f	g	h	i	j	k
1.	12 6	8 8	8 5	7 7	11 8	16 7	6 4	15 9	11 3	6 3	11 5
2.	5 1	13 9	6 6	9 0	8 4	12 5	14 5	13 6	11 2	8 6	11 4
3.	8 1	13 8	7 5	8 2	15 7	12 4	7 0	5 4	9 3	17 9	13 7

17A. Practice Set

▶Subtract.

	a	b	c	d	e	f	g	h	i	j	k
1.	16 9	10 1	14 7	9 1	6 2	15 8	10 9	13 8	11 9	17 8	11 4
2.	10 2	14 8	7 4	13 9	11 2	8 6	15 7	9 6	14 9	10 6	12 8
3.	13 4	11 6	18 9	10 3	12 6	14 5	11 5	13 7	9 2	16 8	10 7
4.	12 5	14 6	10 4	15 9	11 3	12 3	9 9	9 3	10 8	13 6	12 9

RENAMING IN SUBTRACTION

Sometimes you have to rename in order to subtract.

Example: $46 - 8 = ?$ Check your answer.

Solution: To subtract the ones, rename the tens and the ones.

$$\begin{array}{r} \overset{3\ 16}{\cancel{4}\,\cancel{6}} \\ -\ \ 8 \\ \hline 38 \end{array} \qquad \textbf{Check:}\quad \begin{array}{r} 38 \\ +\ 8 \\ \hline 46 \end{array}$$

---

18. Inventory Test

▶Subtract. Check your answers.

	a	b	c	d	e	f	g	h	i	j
1.	21 8	42 7	45 9	28 5	16 7	65 8	27 8	17 8	53 4	71 2
2.	65 9	44 7	83 8	61 7	78 9	60 1	52 7	88 9	11 9	36 9
3.	20 8	15 9	94 6	72 8	23 7	38 9	40 7	30 8	62 5	35 8

18A. Practice Set

▶ Subtract. Check your answers.

	a	b	c	d	e	f	g	h	i	j
1.	42	37	21	70	25	48	74	64	33	11
	4	8	9	3	9	6	9	8	9	8
2.	22	72	84	40	82	45	53	20	31	93
	7	9	5	1	8	6	9	6	4	8
3.	61	15	91	61	76	14	33	66	31	56
	4	6	3	9	8	7	8	8	5	9

RENAMING MORE THAN ONCE IN SUBTRACTION

When subtracting, you sometimes have to rename more than once.

Example: $726 - 487 = ?$

Solution:

1. To subtract the ones, rename the tens and ones.

$$\begin{array}{r} \overset{1\ 16}{7\,\cancel{2}\,\cancel{6}} \\ -4\,8\,7 \\ \hline 9 \end{array}$$

2. To subtract the tens, rename the hundreds and the tens.

$$\begin{array}{r} \overset{6\ 11\ 16}{\cancel{7}\,\cancel{2}\,\cancel{6}} \\ -4\,8\,7 \\ \hline 2\,3\,9 \end{array}$$

---

19. Inventory Test

▶ Subtract. Check your answers.

	a	b	c	d	e	f	g	h
1.	78	92	62	28	296	462	581	130
	35	48	42	19	127	381	362	51
2.	304	211	143	719	922	876	707	800
	95	76	54	534	654	192	641	372
3.	4275	2091	8009	2175	5112	8126	3821	4000
	843	1936	705	1963	3896	5175	1777	2176

19A. Practice Set

▶ Subtract. Check your answers.

	a	b	c	d	e	f	g	h
1.	272 83	411 201	183 85	702 654	181 66	444 55	672 381	400 215
2.	360 275	126 83	470 293	515 418	1342 843	1037 835	6274 3168	2047 139
3.	3628 2416	7142 2685	9082 765	7111 1236	6255 3729	3000 1765	1768 1580	7126 4178
4.	4992 2763	7826 579	5720 208	6113 2781	4132 782	3076 2061	5826 2739	4576 2809

Keeping Pace

▶ Find each answer.

1.
```
  7
  8
  4
  6
 +9
───
```

2.
```
  86
  97
  25
 +48
────
```

3.
```
  3694
   274
   806
 +4695
──────
```

4.
```
   86
 ×  8
─────
```

5.
```
   78
 ×49
─────
```

6.
```
  908
 × 76
─────
```

7.
```
  467
 − 83
─────
```

8.
```
  9000
 −7419
──────
```

9.
```
  8607
 −4328
──────
```

10. The earth revolves around the sun at a rate of approximately 19 miles a second. What is the approximate distance covered by the earth in space in one minute? in one hour?

Stop! Try the Survey Test on page 18 again. See if you can make a perfect score.

Career Capsule

Flight attendants must be able to compute the travel time between cities by using a time-table schedule.

▶ Use the schedule at the right for Exercises **1–3.**

1. How long does it take to get to Kansas City on Flight 457?

2. How long does it take to get to Kansas City on Flight 915?

3. How long does it take to get to Kansas City on Flight 397?

To Kansas City		
Leave	Arrive	Flight Number
8:50 a.m.	10:50 a.m.	915
1:00 p.m.	3:30 p.m.	397
5:00 p.m.	6:55 p.m.	457

APPLICATIONS

Measurement

The tables below show the distance in kilometers between Washington, D.C. and each of nine other cities.

▶ Use these tables for Exercises 1–6.

City	Distance in Kilometers	City	Distance in Kilometers	City	Distance in Kilometers
Augusta	739	Detroit	554	New York	328
Baltimore	41	Los Angeles	3262	San Francisco	3427
Dallas	1683	Miami	1334	Seattle	3221

1. Which city is farthest from Washington, D.C.?

2. Which city is nearest to Washington, D.C.?

▶ In Exercises 3–6, find the difference between the two distances.

3. Washington, D.C. to New York and Washington, D.C. to Los Angeles

4. Washington, D.C. to Seattle and Washington, D.C. to Baltimore

5. Augusta to Washington, D.C. and Miami to Washington, D.C.

6. Dallas to Washington, D.C. and Detroit to Washington, D.C.

The table below gives the approximate areas in square meters of a baseball diamond, a basketball court, a football field, a soccer field, and a tennis court (singles).

	Baseball Diamond	Basketball Court	Football Field	Soccer Field	Tennis Court
Area in Square Meters	752	1450	5351	7525	194

▶ In Exercises 7–14, find the difference in area. Use the table above.

7. A baseball diamond and a tennis court

8. A basketball court and a baseball diamond

9. A soccer field and a football field

10. A football field and a basketball court

11. A soccer field and a baseball diamond

12. A basketball court and a tennis court

13. A football field and a baseball diamond

14. A football field and a tennis court

Division with Whole Numbers

20. Survey Test

▶ Divide.

	a	b	c	d	e	f
1.	8)56	4)24	6)54	9)45	7)0	7)42
2.	4)252	7)581	8)504	5)219	8)248	3)217
3.	5)185	52)1778	47)988	21)5166	177)2407	288)50,776

RELATING MULTIPLICATION AND DIVISION

Division is the **opposite** operation of multiplication. Because of this, you can use multiplication to check division.

Example: 72 ÷ 9 = ?

Solution: Divisor ⟶ 9)72 ⟵ Dividend   **8** ⟵ Quotient   **Check:** 8 × 9 = 72

These should be the same.

---

21. Inventory Test

Basic Division Facts

▶ Divide.

	a	b	c	d	e	f	g
1.	9)54	9)0	7)49	8)64	7)0	9)36	8)40
2.	8)56	7)35	9)18	5)35	9)63	6)36	5)45
3.	6)42	8)24	6)48	8)32	6)30	7)42	9)81
4.	7)21	6)24	7)56	7)14	8)16	9)9	2)16
5.	9)27	4)36	8)72	4)28	7)63	3)12	8)48

21A. Practice Set

▶ Divide.

	a	b	c	d	e	f	g
1.	9)18	6)42	8)16	6)12	7)7	9)45	2)16
2.	6)54	9)54	2)14	7)35	2)8	3)24	5)40
3.	9)63	5)15	7)14	8)24	3)18	3)27	5)30
4.	7)42	8)32	9)0	5)45	7)21	6)18	2)18
5.	8)56	6)30	3)21	6)24	9)9	7)28	6)48
6.	9)36	7)49	9)81	7)63	8)64	6)36	9)72

USING THE BASIC DIVISION FACTS

To help you place the first digit in a quotient, count the number of digits in the divisor. Then draw a line after the same number of digits in the dividend. In the Examples below, the **X** tells where to place the first digit.

Examples: 4)7|28   8)9|00   48)76|37

The following show when you may have to draw a new line.

Examples: 9)5|67 ◄—— Since 5 is less than 9,

5)2|05 ◄—— Since 2 is less than 5,

9)56|7 ◄—— Draw the line after the 6.

5)20|5 ◄—— Draw the line after the 0.

Example: 368 ÷ 8 = ? Check your answer.

Solution: 1. 8)3|68 ◄—— 3 is less than 8. Draw the line after the 6.

2.
$$
\begin{array}{r}
4\,6 \\
8\overline{)36\,8} \\
32 \\
\hline
48 \\
48 \\
\hline
0
\end{array}
$$

3. **Check:**
$$
\begin{array}{r}
46 \\
\times\ 8 \\
\hline
368
\end{array}
$$

22. Inventory Test

Divisors—One Digit

▶ Divide. Check your answers.

	a	b	c	d	e	f	g
1.	2)188	8)176	7)224	5)600	6)252	8)200	5)205
2.	4)728	6)366	3)279	7)357	4)204	6)546	3)234
3.	4)224	8)736	9)711	8)288	9)216	5)175	6)504

22A. Practice Set

▶ Divide. Check your answers.

	a	b	c	d	e	f
1.	5)225	2)182	4)624	7)427	9)225	8)616
2.	3)339	8)464	5)400	6)324	9)117	4)408
3.	4)144	7)189	9)315	2)624	6)342	7)455
4.	4)376	6)204	7)637	9)207	5)785	8)432

DIVISION WITH REMAINDERS OTHER THAN ZERO

Sometimes a division problem has a remainder other than zero.

Example: $265 \div 9 = ?$ Check your answer.

This is how you write the answer.

```
            29  r 4
Solution: 9)265
            18
           ---
            85
            81
           ---
             4   ←— Remainder
```

Check:
```
      29
   ×   9
   -----
     261
   +   4   ←— Add the remainder.
   -----        This should be the
     265   ←—   same as the dividend.
```

---

23. Inventory Test

Division with Remainders Other than Zero

▶ Divide. Check your answers.

	a	b	c	d	e	f
1.	5)274	3)112	2)183	6)104	7)709	9)412
2.	6)723	4)107	2)211	9)273	5)272	8)111
3.	7)346	4)147	6)526	3)760	4)178	6)283
4.	8)2165	4)153	5)1623	3)296	9)714	6)2122
5.	8)2095	3)2172	9)381	9)1302	7)150	8)7214
6.	4)399	7)1526	8)757	6)518	9)4215	5)2117
7.	5)871	9)1018	8)623	7)485	6)4810	7)3905

23A. Practice Set

▶ Divide. Check your answers.

	a	b	c	d	e	f
1.	3)535	2)643	5)524	2)305	4)681	6)609
2.	7)803	5)508	7)503	6)784	9)327	4)807
3.	8)1009	5)714	4)538	9)620	8)484	7)211
4.	5)666	8)182	7)717	4)562	9)303	6)1682
5.	2)7215	3)1162	4)2125	8)1003	6)2155	5)1778
6.	7)5244	6)2119	9)2134	3)7261	8)1723	4)3393
7.	5)4306	3)9714	6)2071	4)3219	7)9216	8)7923

FINDING THE AVERAGE

To find the **average,** or **mean,** of two or more numbers, first find the sum. Then divide by the number of numbers.

Example: Find the average of 14, 12, 7, 9, 16, and 8.

Solution: Step 1: Find the sum. $14 + 12 + 7 + 9 + 16 + 8 = 66$

Step 2: There are 6 numbers. Divide the sum by 6.

$$\underset{6\overline{)66}}{\textbf{11}} \longleftarrow \text{ Average}$$

24. Inventory Test

▶ Find the average.

a	b	c
1. 4, 5, 7, 8	10, 14, 18	8, 5, 7, 2, 3
2. 5, 8, 11	6, 17, 5, 12	18, 17, 19
3. 6, 2, 7, 9	4, 0, 2, 6	1, 2, 3, 4, 5
4. 11, 9, 3, 15	20, 52, 24	96, 4, 20
5. 12, 9, 8, 7	15, 10, 5	32, 20, 11

24A. Practice Set

▶ Find the average.

a	b	c
1. 24, 18, 18	0, 2, 4, 6	7, 12, 15, 10
2. 4, 8, 12, 22, 14	16, 27, 5	96, 73, 83
3. 5, 0, 4	5, 10, 25, 40, 10	96, 100
4. 72, 60, 85, 91	8, 0, 8, 8	4, 80, 7, 12, 27
5. 4, 17, 21, 6	26, 19, 45	8, 7, 6, 0, 14

Career Capsule

Consumer consultants often work for Consumer Protection Agencies. They keep consumers informed about **average costs.**

▶ In Exercises **1–4,** find the average cost.

1. New cars: $20,694; $6,489; $7,810; $12,555
2. Three-bedroom house: $65,000; $110,000; $68,985; $85,875
3. Automobile operating costs per mile: 33¢;   45¢;   30¢;   35¢
4. Public transportation—one fare: 50¢;   40¢;   75¢;   45¢

27

DIVISION—LARGER DIVISORS

To divide with larger numbers, follow the same steps as in the Examples on pages 24 and 25.

Example: 7637 ÷ 48 = ? Check your answer.

Solution:
$$\begin{array}{r} 159 \text{ r } 5 \\ 48\overline{)7637} \\ \underline{48} \\ 283 \\ \underline{240} \\ 437 \\ \underline{432} \\ 5 \end{array}$$

Check:
$$\begin{array}{r} 159 \\ \times\ 48 \\ \hline 1272 \\ 6360 \\ \hline 7632 \\ +\ \ \ 5 \\ \hline 7637 \end{array}$$

Same as the dividend.

25. Inventory Test

▶ Divide. Check your answers.

	a	b	c	d	e	f
1.	12)375	14)215	21)882	57)4617	62)2943	23)943
2.	18)5062	81)4617	34)578	70)7030	49)1312	74)3035
3.	84)6300	53)7228	25)1775	48)2593	35)9625	96)2176
4.	21)1176	34)1632	59)4240	62)7626	46)3723	93)4185

25A. Practice Set

▶ Divide. Check your answers.

	a	b	c	d	e	f
1.	65)2866	85)6091	11)465	21)1099	31)1922	41)1365
2.	22)935	32)1664	11)2848	42)7659	77)7854	78)9759
3.	94)9212	83)2454	29)2407	63)8820	54)4032	19)4914
4.	51)8007	45)4590	84)9248	12)10,482	92)3496	46)11,316

25B. Practice Set

More Challenging Exercises

▶ Divide. Check your answers.

	a	b	c	d	e
1.	75)4216	82)10,341	53)9682	47)12,307	98)3268
2.	114)7638	235)8460	562)9554	756)9828	289)9248
3.	224)56,224	351)90,207	199)39,601	556)24,464	659)96,873
4.	223)25,649	416)56,993	567)64,648	196)50,786	493)97,628

Keeping Pace

▶ Find the answers.

1.	2.	3.	4.	5.
78	8764	4723	2000	48
46	875	−1804	− 892	×26
99	2362			
+45	+7407			

6.	7.	8.	9.
709	8)736	49)7265	72)7236
× 48			

10. In nine basketball games, Alma Ramirez scored 85 field goals (2 points each) and 64 foul shots (1 point each). What is her point average per game?

Stop! Repeat the Survey Test on page 23. See if you can make a perfect score.

Career Capsule

Travel agents must be able to compute travel time to help people plan trips.

▶ For each trip in Exercises **1–6,** the car is driven at an **average rate** of 45 miles per hour. Find the travel time.

Example: Atlanta to Boston: 990 miles

Solution: Time = Distance ÷ Rate

Time = 990 ÷ 45

Time = **22 hours**

1. Detroit to Dallas: 1170 miles

2. Seattle to Omaha: 1620 miles

3. Toledo to Dallas: 1035 miles

4. New York to Los Angeles: 2790 miles

5. Louisville to Denver: 1125 miles

6. Tulsa to Boston: 1530 miles

APPLICATIONS

Transportation

▶ In Exercises **1–12,** find the time for each trip.

Example: Chicago to Cincinnati, a distance of 474 kilometers by train at 79 kilometers per hour

Solution: Time $= \frac{\text{Distance}}{\text{Rate}}$

Time $= \frac{474}{79}$

Time $=$ **6 hours**

Buffalo to Washington, D.C., a distance of 600 kilometers

1. By train at 50 kilometers per hour

2. By motorcycle at 60 kilometers per hour

3. By car at 75 kilometers per hour

4. By plane at 300 kilometers per hour

Atlanta to Chicago, a distance of 1140 kilometers

5. By car at 76 kilometers per hour

6. By train at 57 kilometers per hour

7. By plane at 570 kilometers per hour

8. By motorcycle at 60 kilometers per hour

Washington, D.C. to Atlanta, a distance of 1032 kilometers

9. By train at 129 kilometers per hour

10. By car at 86 kilometers per hour

11. By plane at 516 kilometers per hour

12. By motorcycle at 60 kilometers per hour

Food

▶ Find the better buy.

Example: Rolls

8 for 49 <u>or</u> 10 for 55¢

Solution: Find the cost of 1 roll.

$8\overline{)49}$ 6 r 1   <u>or</u> $10\overline{)55}$ 5 r 5

Better buy: **10 for 55¢**

13. Cucumbers
3 for 29¢ <u>or</u> 5 for 55¢

14. Corn
4 ears for 49¢ <u>or</u> 6 ears for 89¢

15. Grapefruit
2 for 39¢ <u>or</u> 10 for 99¢

16. Oranges
5 for 89¢ <u>or</u> 6 for 99¢

17. Lemons
12 for 89¢ <u>or</u> 4 for 52¢

18. Frankfurters
8 for 69¢ <u>or</u> 10 for 99¢

▶ Choose the correct answer. Choose **a**, **b**, **c**, or **d**.

The table below gives the base price and the cost of five options on a new luxury car.

Use this table for Exercises **1–7**.

	OPTIONS				
Base Price	Cruise Control	Power Windows	Four-note Horn	Stereo Radio	AM Radio
$8,850	$108	$205	$23	$340	$68

1. Find the cost of this car with a stereo radio.
   a. $9190   **b.** $8918   **c.** $8190   **d.** $8818

2. What is the cost of this car with cruise control and power windows?
   a. $9055   **b.** $8958   **c.** $313   **d.** $9163

3. Find the cost of this car with the AM radio and power windows.
   a. $9013   **b.** $9123   **c.** $9023   **d.** $9395

4. Find the difference between the cost of power windows and cruise control.
   a. $197   **b.** $313   **c.** $97   **d.** $104

5. Find the difference between the cost of the AM radio and the stereo radio.
   a. $182   **b.** $272   **c.** $172   **d.** $282

6. What is the cost of this car with a four-note horn, stereo radio, and cruise control?
   a. $9213   **b.** $9048   **c.** $9321   **d.** $8981

7. Find the total cost of the first four options.
   a. $9523   **b.** $676   **c.** $744   **d.** $666

8. The Gordon family pays $255 per month for rent, $48 for utilities, and $23 for fire insurance.
   Find the total of these expenses.
   a. $216   **b.** $226   **c.** $316   **d.** $326

9. The distance between Washington, D.C. and San Francisco is 3427 kilometers. The distance between Washington, D.C. and Los Angeles is 3262 kilometers.
   How many kilometers farther from Washington, D.C. is San Francisco?
   a. 65   **b.** 265   **c.** 155   **d.** 165

10. The area of a badminton court is 880 square feet for doubles and 748 square feet for singles.
Find the difference in square feet between the two areas.

    a. 232   **b.** 132   **c.** 142   **d.** 32

11. The area of a tennis court is 2808 square feet for doubles and 2106 square feet for singles.
Find the difference in square feet between the two areas.

    a. 502   **b.** 602   **c.** 702   **d.** 692

12. Sharon eats 3 eggs in one week. One egg contains 77 calories.
How many calories are there in 3 eggs?

    a. 221   **b.** 211   **c.** 154   **d.** 231

13. Bruce drinks 28 glasses of milk in one week. Each glass of milk contains 159 calories.
How many calories are there in 28 glasses of milk?

    a. 2882   **b.** 4352   **c.** 3352   **d.** 4452

The bar graph below shows Maria's monthly income for the years 1980–1983.

▶ Use this graph for Exercises **14–16.**

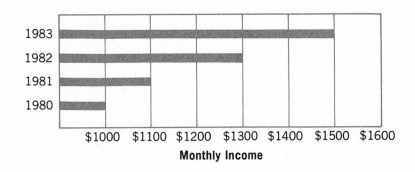

14. In what year was Maria's monthly income the least?

    a. 1980   **b.** 1981   **c.** 1982   **d.** 1983

15. In what year was Maria's monthly income the greatest?

    a. 1980   **b.** 1981   **c.** 1982   **d.** 1983

16. Maria earned $1500 per month in 1983.
How much did she earn during the first six months of 1983?

    a. $9000   **b.** $8000   **c.** $7500   **d.** $900

17. The distance from Washington, D.C. to Miami is 1650 kilometers. Mrs. Ruiz travels this distance by plane at 550 kilometers per hour.
Find her time in hours for the trip.

    a. 24   **b.** 1   **c.** 2   **d.** 3

18. The distance from Atlanta to Chicago is 1053 kilometers. Mr. Lightfoot makes the trip by car at 81 kilometers per hour. Find his time in hours for the trip.

a. 14   **b.** 23   **c.** 12   **d.** 13

19. The distance from Detroit to Washington, D.C. is 550 kilometers. Dan makes the trip by motorcycle at 50 kilometers per hour. Find his time in hours for the trip.

a. 3   **b.** 11   **c.** 2   **d.** 10

20. Find the best buy.
   a. 2 cucumbers for 54¢   **b.** 3 cucumbers for 78¢
   c. 1 cucumber for 25¢   **d.** 4 cucumbers for 96¢

21. Find the best buy.
   a. 6 oranges for 84¢   **b.** 5 oranges for 99¢
   c. 4 oranges for 75¢   **d.** 3 oranges for 61¢

22. Find the best buy.
   a. 6 lemons for 89¢   **b.** 5 lemons for 99¢
   c. 4 lemons for 68¢   **d.** 3 lemons for 54¢

23. A painting is 27 centimeters long and 22 centimeters wide.
Find the distance in centimeters around the painting.

   a. 88   **b.** 49
   c. 594   **d.** 98

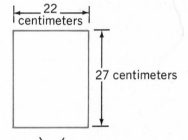

24. Each side of this pentagon is 9 meters long.
Find the perimeter of the pentagon in meters.

   a. 45   **b.** 27
   c. 36   **d.** 81

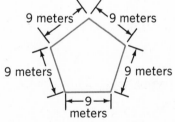

25. A bedroom is 6 meters long and 6 meters wide.
Find the number of square meters in the area of the bedroom.

   a. 18   **b.** 36
   c. 12   **d.** 24

26. A playroom is 8 meters long and 5 meters wide.
Find its area in square meters.

   a. 26   **b.** 13
   c. 40   **d.** 39

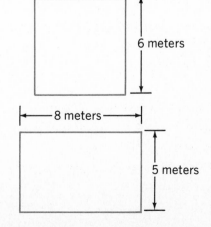

REVIEW OF SKILLS: Whole Numbers

▶ Complete this puzzle. Write the answers to the exercises in the boxes of the puzzle. The answers should check across and down. Each box holds one digit.

ACROSS

1. $864 \div 12 =$ ___
2. $28\overline{)336} =$ ___
4. $312 - 295 =$ ___
6. $74 \times 26 =$ ___
7. $19 + 28 =$ ___
8. $1544 - 1019 =$ ___
10. $8350 \div 835 =$ ___
11. $11 \times 11 =$ ___
13. $128 + 476 + 218 + 170 =$ ___
16. $20{,}202 \div 259 =$ ___
18. $8017 - 7982 =$ ___
19. $19 \times 12 =$ ___
21. $319 + 187 =$ ___
22. $15\overline{)225} =$ ___
24. $1556 - 1314 =$ ___
26. $19{,}152 \div 798 =$ ___
28. $10{,}000 - 5175 =$ ___
30. $11 \times 6 =$ ___
31. $7 \times 7 \times 2 =$ ___
32. $101 - 83 =$ ___

DOWN

1. $2588 - 1883 =$ ___
2. $96 \div 8 =$ ___
3. $2 \times 2 \times 2 \times 3 =$ ___
4. $13\overline{)182} =$ ___
5. $13{,}412 - 5683 =$ ___
6. $5 \times 5 \times 3 \times 2 =$ ___
9. $7\overline{)147} =$ ___
11. $3094 \div 17 =$ ___
12. $90 - 75 =$ ___
14. $1364 - 428 =$ ___
15. $25\overline{)625} =$ ___
16. $24 + 19 + 29 =$ ___
17. $2040 \div 24 =$ ___
20. $12{,}497 - 3971 =$ ___
22. $5 \times 5 \times 5 =$ ___
23. $2 \times 3 \times 3 \times 3 =$ ___
25. $8 \times 31 =$ ___
27. $88\overline{)4048} =$ ___
28. $106 - 57 =$ ___
29. $25 \times 88 =$ ___ $\times 25$

Renaming Fractions

26. Survey Test

1. Write a fraction to tell what part of each figure is shaded.

a   b

2. Which pairs name equivalent fractions?

   a $\frac{2}{3}, \frac{14}{21}$ b $\frac{20}{25}, \frac{10}{15}$

   c $\frac{7}{8}, \frac{42}{48}$ d $\frac{15}{10}, \frac{3}{2}$

3. Express in higher terms.

   a $\frac{2}{3} = \frac{}{27}$ b $\frac{7}{18} = \frac{}{54}$

4. Express in lowest terms.

   a $\frac{7}{28}$ b $\frac{18}{24}$

5. Express as fractions.

   a $8\frac{2}{3}$ b $7\frac{5}{8}$ c $6 = \frac{}{4}$

6. Express as mixed numerals.

   a $\frac{17}{2}$ b $\frac{8}{3}$ c $\frac{24}{10}$

WRITING FRACTIONS

The figure at the right is divided into 5 equal parts. Three of the 5 parts are shaded.

$\frac{3}{5}$ of the figure is shaded.

A numeral such as $\frac{3}{5}$ is called a **fraction**. A fraction has a **numerator** and a **denominator**.

$\frac{3}{5}$ ← Numerator
$\frac{}{}$ ← Denominator

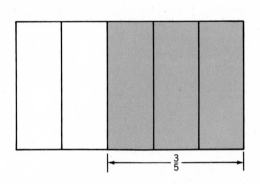

---

27. Inventory Test

▶ Write a fraction to tell what part of each figure is shaded.

1.   **2.** 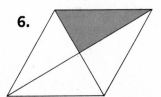   **3.** 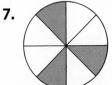   **4.**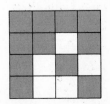

5.    **6.** 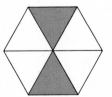   **7.** 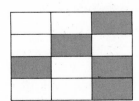   **8.**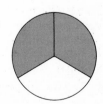

27A. Practice Set

▶ Write a fraction to tell what part of each figure is shaded.

1.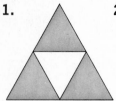
2.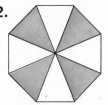
3.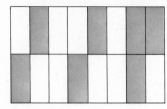
4.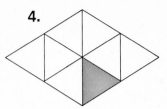

5.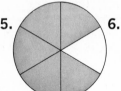
6.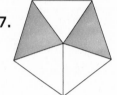
7.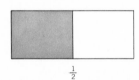
8.

EQUIVALENT FRACTIONS

Equivalent fractions name the same number.

$$\frac{1}{2} = \frac{2}{4} = \frac{4}{8}$$ ◀—— Equivalent fractions

$\frac{1}{2}$ $\frac{2}{4}$ $\frac{4}{8}$

You can check whether two fractions are equivalent by **comparing cross products. Equivalent fractions have equal cross products.**

Check		Check	
$\frac{2}{4} \bowtie \frac{4}{8}$	$4 \times 4 = 16$ $2 \times 8 = 16$	$\frac{7}{16} \bowtie \frac{3}{8}$	$16 \times 3 = 48$ $7 \times 8 = 56$

$\frac{2}{4}$ is **equivalent** to $\frac{4}{8}$. $\frac{7}{16}$ is **not equivalent** to $\frac{3}{8}$.

---

28. Inventory Test

▶ Tell whether or not the fractions of each pair are equivalent.

	a	b	c	d	e
1.	$\frac{1}{2}, \frac{16}{32}$	$\frac{8}{24}, \frac{1}{4}$	$\frac{2}{3}, \frac{10}{15}$	$\frac{3}{8}, \frac{9}{25}$	$\frac{20}{25}, \frac{3}{5}$
2.	$\frac{15}{20}, \frac{3}{4}$	$\frac{12}{16}, \frac{2}{3}$	$\frac{1}{8}, \frac{4}{32}$	$\frac{8}{16}, \frac{7}{14}$	$\frac{5}{9}, \frac{10}{16}$
3.	$\frac{3}{5}, \frac{12}{20}$	$\frac{18}{36}, \frac{5}{8}$	$\frac{3}{10}, \frac{9}{30}$	$\frac{4}{6}, \frac{6}{9}$	$\frac{13}{15}, \frac{6}{7}$

28A. Practice Set

▶ Tell whether or not the fractions of each pair are equivalent.

	a	b	c	d	e
1.	$\frac{12}{16}, \frac{3}{4}$	$\frac{5}{10}, \frac{2}{4}$	$\frac{18}{24}, \frac{6}{8}$	$\frac{3}{4}, \frac{21}{28}$	$\frac{8}{32}, \frac{1}{8}$
2.	$\frac{7}{28}, \frac{1}{4}$	$\frac{1}{5}, \frac{4}{25}$	$\frac{10}{100}, \frac{8}{80}$	$\frac{9}{64}, \frac{3}{8}$	$\frac{7}{20}, \frac{21}{60}$
3.	$\frac{4}{5}, \frac{8}{10}$	$\frac{2}{3}, \frac{9}{12}$	$\frac{16}{25}, \frac{4}{5}$	$\frac{8}{10}, \frac{16}{20}$	$\frac{5}{18}, \frac{20}{72}$

WRITING FRACTIONS IN HIGHER TERMS

To find an equivalent fraction in higher terms, multiply the numerator and denominator by the <u>same</u> number.

Example: $\frac{5}{6} = \frac{}{48}$

Solution: Since 6 must be multiplied by 8 to get 48, multiply 5 by 8.

$$\frac{5}{6} = \frac{5 \times 8}{6 \times 8} = \frac{40}{48}$$

$\frac{5}{6}$ and $\frac{40}{48}$ are **equivalent.**

Example: $\frac{15}{16} = \frac{}{96}$

Solution: Since 16 must be multiplied by 6 to get 96, multiply 15 by 6.

$$\frac{15}{16} = \frac{15 \times 6}{16 \times 6} = \frac{90}{96}$$

$\frac{15}{16}$ and $\frac{90}{96}$ are **equivalent.**

---

29. Inventory Test

▶ Make the fractions equivalent.

	a	b	c	d	e
1.	$\frac{1}{2} = \frac{}{6}$	$\frac{2}{3} = \frac{}{12}$	$\frac{1}{5} = \frac{}{30}$	$\frac{3}{4} = \frac{}{16}$	$\frac{5}{8} = \frac{}{16}$
2.	$\frac{2}{3} = \frac{}{15}$	$\frac{1}{8} = \frac{}{48}$	$\frac{3}{4} = \frac{}{24}$	$\frac{5}{6} = \frac{}{36}$	$\frac{3}{8} = \frac{}{24}$
3.	$\frac{4}{5} = \frac{}{20}$	$\frac{7}{8} = \frac{}{40}$	$\frac{3}{5} = \frac{}{25}$	$\frac{1}{8} = \frac{}{32}$	$\frac{1}{3} = \frac{}{27}$
4.	$\frac{7}{16} = \frac{}{48}$	$\frac{5}{9} = \frac{}{36}$	$\frac{12}{17} = \frac{}{34}$	$\frac{7}{10} = \frac{}{100}$	$\frac{3}{7} = \frac{}{42}$

29A. Practice Set

▶ Make the fractions equivalent.

	a	b	c	d	e
1.	$\frac{3}{4} = \frac{}{8}$	$\frac{2}{3} = \frac{}{6}$	$\frac{5}{8} = \frac{}{24}$	$\frac{1}{3} = \frac{}{36}$	$\frac{1}{16} = \frac{}{32}$
2.	$\frac{5}{12} = \frac{}{36}$	$\frac{3}{8} = \frac{}{32}$	$\frac{4}{9} = \frac{}{45}$	$\frac{1}{2} = \frac{}{42}$	$\frac{3}{5} = \frac{}{35}$
3.	$\frac{4}{7} = \frac{}{21}$	$\frac{3}{11} = \frac{}{33}$	$\frac{5}{6} = \frac{}{42}$	$\frac{2}{3} = \frac{}{18}$	$\frac{7}{12} = \frac{}{48}$
4.	$\frac{7}{16} = \frac{}{32}$	$\frac{1}{12} = \frac{}{60}$	$\frac{3}{8} = \frac{}{72}$	$\frac{1}{5} = \frac{}{100}$	$\frac{5}{9} = \frac{}{99}$

WRITING FRACTIONS IN LOWEST TERMS

To find an equivalent fraction in **lower terms,** divide the numerator and denominator by the <u>same</u> number.

$$\frac{12}{36} = \frac{12 \div 3}{36 \div 3} = \frac{4}{12} \longleftarrow \text{Lower terms} \qquad \frac{12}{36} = \frac{12 \div 4}{36 \div 4} = \frac{3}{9} \longleftarrow \text{Lower terms}$$

A fraction is in **lowest terms** if the numerator and denominator have no common factors other than 1.

Example: Write $\frac{24}{30}$ in lowest terms.

Solution: $\frac{24}{30} = \frac{24 \div 6}{30 \div 6} = \frac{4}{5} \longleftarrow$ Lowest terms because $4 = 4 \times 1$ and $5 = 5 \times 1$. The only common factor is 1.

Another Way

$$\frac{24}{30} = \frac{24 \div 3}{30 \div 3} = \frac{8}{10} \longleftarrow \text{Lower terms}$$

$$\frac{8}{10} = \frac{8 \div 2}{10 \div 2} = \frac{4}{5} \longleftarrow \text{Lowest terms}$$

---

30. Inventory Test

▶ Write each fraction in lowest terms.

	a	b	c	d	e	f	g	h
1.	$\frac{3}{6}$	$\frac{8}{12}$	$\frac{9}{24}$	$\frac{10}{15}$	$\frac{8}{16}$	$\frac{9}{36}$	$\frac{7}{21}$	$\frac{14}{21}$
2.	$\frac{4}{10}$	$\frac{12}{36}$	$\frac{20}{25}$	$\frac{20}{24}$	$\frac{6}{36}$	$\frac{25}{35}$	$\frac{4}{24}$	$\frac{4}{32}$
3.	$\frac{26}{39}$	$\frac{18}{36}$	$\frac{15}{24}$	$\frac{20}{36}$	$\frac{14}{24}$	$\frac{21}{24}$	$\frac{18}{72}$	$\frac{8}{40}$
4.	$\frac{9}{18}$	$\frac{20}{22}$	$\frac{16}{48}$	$\frac{12}{32}$	$\frac{45}{75}$	$\frac{6}{20}$	$\frac{15}{24}$	$\frac{14}{28}$

30A. Practice Set

▶ Write each fraction in lowest terms.

	a	b	c	d	e	f	g	h
1.	$\frac{6}{12}$	$\frac{5}{20}$	$\frac{20}{28}$	$\frac{16}{24}$	$\frac{15}{25}$	$\frac{27}{36}$	$\frac{7}{42}$	$\frac{25}{50}$
2.	$\frac{8}{24}$	$\frac{16}{18}$	$\frac{15}{45}$	$\frac{24}{32}$	$\frac{27}{45}$	$\frac{3}{15}$	$\frac{25}{125}$	$\frac{21}{35}$
3.	$\frac{20}{26}$	$\frac{5}{35}$	$\frac{32}{64}$	$\frac{8}{64}$	$\frac{7}{28}$	$\frac{28}{32}$	$\frac{50}{75}$	$\frac{18}{48}$
4.	$\frac{17}{51}$	$\frac{25}{55}$	$\frac{16}{54}$	$\frac{9}{54}$	$\frac{8}{80}$	$\frac{10}{25}$	$\frac{13}{52}$	$\frac{14}{35}$

WRITING FRACTIONS FOR MIXED NUMERALS

You can write a fraction for a mixed numeral.

$\frac{3}{3}$ $\frac{3}{3}$ $\frac{3}{3}$

$\frac{3}{3}$ $\frac{3}{3}$ $\frac{2}{3}$

Example: Write a fraction for $5\frac{2}{3}$.

Solution: Step 1: Multiply the whole number, 5, and the denominator, 3.

$3 \times 5 = 15$

Step 2: Add the numerator, 2, to the answer to Step 1.

$2 + 15 = 17$

Step 3: Write the answer to Step 2 over the denominator, 3.

$\frac{17}{3}$

---

31. Inventory Test

▶ Write a fraction for each mixed numeral.

	a	b	c	d
1.	$2\frac{1}{2} = \frac{}{2}$	$3\frac{1}{4} = \frac{}{4}$	$1\frac{3}{4} = \frac{}{4}$	$4\frac{2}{3} = \frac{}{3}$
2.	$2\frac{2}{3} = \frac{}{3}$	$4 = \frac{}{2}$	$5\frac{1}{4} = \frac{}{4}$	$7\frac{1}{2} = \frac{}{2}$
3.	$6 = \frac{}{3}$	$3\frac{7}{8} = \frac{}{8}$	$6\frac{3}{8} = \frac{}{8}$	$5 = \frac{}{6}$
4.	$4\frac{3}{5} = \frac{}{5}$	$2 = \frac{}{16}$	$4\frac{3}{16} = \frac{}{16}$	$2\frac{5}{6} = \frac{}{6}$

31A. Practice Set

▶ Write a fraction for each mixed numeral.

	a	b	c	d
1.	$2\frac{1}{4} = \frac{\ }{4}$	$3 = \frac{\ }{5}$	$2\frac{5}{8} = \frac{\ }{8}$	$1\frac{1}{16} = \frac{\ }{16}$
2.	$8\frac{1}{4} = \frac{\ }{4}$	$5\frac{3}{5} = \frac{\ }{5}$	$3\frac{3}{16} = \frac{\ }{16}$	$7 = \frac{\ }{2}$
3.	$5\frac{2}{3} = \frac{\ }{3}$	$7\frac{1}{6} = \frac{\ }{6}$	$9\frac{3}{4} = \frac{\ }{4}$	$2\frac{13}{16} = \frac{\ }{16}$
4.	$7\frac{1}{12} = \frac{\ }{12}$	$2 = \frac{\ }{7}$	$8\frac{4}{5} = \frac{\ }{5}$	$12\frac{1}{5} = \frac{\ }{5}$

Career Capsule

A **payroll clerk** has to know the number of hours worked by each employee in order to compute weekly earnings.

▶ In Exercises **1–9,** find the hours and minutes worked. Then write a mixed numeral for the hours and minutes.

Example: In Out

Solution: In–9:00   Out–1:15

Hours worked: 9:00–12:00: 3 hr.
                12:00–1:15: 1 hr. 15 min.
                Total: 4 hr. 15 min.

4 hr. 15 min. = $4\frac{15}{60}$ hr., or **$4\frac{1}{4}$ hr.**

1. In   Out

2. In   Out

3. In   Out

4. In   Out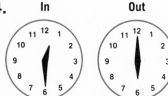

5. In   Out

6. In   Out

7. In   Out

8. In   Out

9. In   Out

40

FRACTIONS GREATER THAN ONE

To write a mixed numeral or a whole number for a fraction, first divide the numerator of the fraction by the denominator. If there is a remainder, write it over the divisor. Write the fraction in lowest terms.

Examples: Write a mixed numeral or a whole number for each fraction.

a. $\frac{18}{6}$ b. $\frac{19}{8}$

Solutions: Divide the numerator by the denominator.

a. $\frac{18}{6} \longrightarrow$ $6\overline{)18}$ with quotient 3, 18, remainder 0

b. $\frac{19}{8} \longrightarrow$ $8\overline{)19}$ with quotient $2\frac{3}{8}$, 16, remainder 3

$\frac{18}{6} = 3 \longleftarrow$ Whole number $\frac{19}{8} = 2\frac{3}{8} \longleftarrow$ Mixed numeral

32. Inventory Test

▶ Write a mixed numeral or a whole number for each fraction.

	a	b	c	d	e	f	g	h
1.	$\frac{12}{6}$	$\frac{8}{2}$	$\frac{12}{3}$	$\frac{16}{3}$	$\frac{25}{4}$	$\frac{5}{2}$	$\frac{7}{3}$	$\frac{12}{5}$
2.	$\frac{15}{3}$	$\frac{8}{3}$	$\frac{9}{4}$	$\frac{5}{4}$	$\frac{7}{4}$	$\frac{12}{2}$	$\frac{16}{5}$	$\frac{18}{3}$
3.	$\frac{9}{6}$	$\frac{15}{2}$	$\frac{17}{5}$	$\frac{13}{6}$	$\frac{9}{8}$	$\frac{24}{8}$	$\frac{19}{7}$	$\frac{21}{6}$
4.	$\frac{13}{12}$	$\frac{18}{16}$	$\frac{16}{9}$	$\frac{15}{12}$	$\frac{7}{6}$	$\frac{14}{7}$	$\frac{11}{2}$	$\frac{9}{3}$
5.	$\frac{9}{5}$	$\frac{14}{3}$	$\frac{21}{11}$	$\frac{30}{6}$	$\frac{19}{8}$	$\frac{43}{10}$	$\frac{29}{4}$	$\frac{50}{6}$

32A. Practice Set

▶ Write a mixed numeral or a whole number for each fraction.

	a	b	c	d	e	f	g	h
1.	$\frac{7}{7}$	$\frac{8}{5}$	$\frac{12}{7}$	$\frac{18}{6}$	$\frac{12}{11}$	$\frac{11}{4}$	$\frac{27}{5}$	$\frac{20}{6}$
2.	$\frac{5}{3}$	$\frac{13}{4}$	$\frac{17}{3}$	$\frac{17}{8}$	$\frac{20}{4}$	$\frac{18}{5}$	$\frac{17}{15}$	$\frac{21}{9}$
3.	$\frac{25}{6}$	$\frac{21}{8}$	$\frac{9}{2}$	$\frac{23}{17}$	$\frac{16}{7}$	$\frac{28}{7}$	$\frac{30}{12}$	$\frac{12}{10}$
4.	$\frac{23}{6}$	$\frac{35}{7}$	$\frac{26}{8}$	$\frac{30}{7}$	$\frac{13}{3}$	$\frac{48}{18}$	$\frac{32}{10}$	$\frac{16}{10}$
5.	$\frac{41}{7}$	$\frac{19}{17}$	$\frac{33}{8}$	$\frac{51}{2}$	$\frac{27}{27}$	$\frac{40}{30}$	$\frac{22}{11}$	$\frac{39}{5}$

▶ Find the answers.

1. 8963
    745
    2098
    +1776

2. 708
    × 65

3. 47)9263

4. 8607
    −4715

5. Write a fraction to tell what part of the figure is shaded.

6. Make the fractions equivalent. $\frac{5}{15} = \frac{}{45}$
7. Write in lowest terms. a $\frac{32}{40} =$ b $\frac{24}{60} =$
8. Replace with an equivalent mixed numeral. a $\frac{15}{6} =$ b $\frac{25}{4} =$
9. Replace with an equivalent fraction. $4\frac{7}{8} =$
10. Arrange in order, beginning with the least. $\frac{17}{24}, \frac{2}{3}, \frac{5}{8}, \frac{31}{48}, \frac{11}{16}, \frac{3}{4}$

Stop! Try the Survey Test on page 35 again. See if you can make a perfect score.

Career Capsule

Architects use angles when they design homes, office buildings, factories, and the like. A **protractor** is used to measure angles. Angles are measured in **degrees** (°). Since a protractor has 180° and a circle has 360°, the protractor is $\frac{180}{360}$, or $\frac{1}{2}$ of a circle.

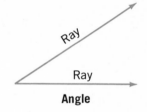

Ray

Ray

Angle

▶ In Exercises **1–3,** read the measure of each angle.

Example:

Solution:

The measure is 60° and not 120°.
You read the "outside" measure when the bottom ray points to the right.

Bottom ray

1. The measure of this angle is $\frac{1}{4}$ of a circle.

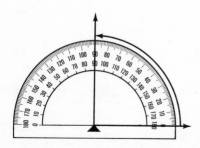

2. The measure of this angle is $\frac{1}{3}$ of a circle.

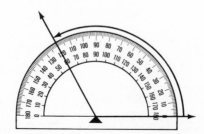

3. The measure of this angle is $\frac{1}{8}$ of a circle.

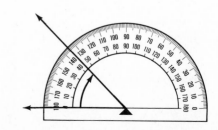

Addition with Fractions

33. Survey Test

▶ Add. Write your answers in lowest terms.

	a	b	c	d	e	f	g
1.	$\frac{5}{8}$	$\frac{1}{6}$	$\frac{5}{6}$	$\frac{2}{3}$	$\frac{3}{4}$	$\frac{2}{3}$	$\frac{5}{6}$
	$\frac{1}{8}$	$\frac{3}{6}$	$\frac{5}{6}$	$\frac{1}{6}$	$\frac{5}{8}$	$\frac{3}{4}$	$\frac{7}{8}$

	a	b	c	d	e	f	g
2.	$\frac{2}{3}$	$\frac{5}{16}$	$\frac{2}{5}$	$\frac{2}{3}$		$4\frac{1}{2}$	$2\frac{1}{4}$
	$\frac{3}{4}$	$\frac{3}{8}$	$\frac{3}{4}$	$\frac{5}{16}$	$3\frac{2}{3}$	$2\frac{5}{6}$	$7\frac{5}{16}$
	$\frac{1}{8}$	$\frac{1}{2}$	$\frac{5}{8}$	$\frac{1}{2}$	$4\frac{5}{8}$	$3\frac{7}{12}$	$4\frac{3}{8}$

	a	b	c
3.	$\frac{5}{12} + \frac{2}{3} =$	$\frac{7}{8} + \frac{2}{3} + \frac{3}{4} =$	$2\frac{1}{2} + 1\frac{7}{12} + 2\frac{5}{18} =$

ADDITION—LIKE FRACTIONS

Like fractions are fractions that have the same denominator.
To add like fractions, first add the numerators. Write this sum over the denominator.

To add mixed numerals, first add the fractions. Then add the whole numbers.

Examples: a. $\frac{3}{8} + \frac{1}{8} = ?$ b. $2\frac{3}{4} + 3\frac{3}{4} = ?$

Solutions: a. $\begin{array}{r} \frac{3}{8} \\ +\frac{1}{8} \\ \hline \frac{4}{8} = \frac{1}{2} \end{array}$ ←——— Lowest terms

b. $\begin{array}{r} 2\frac{3}{4} \\ +3\frac{3}{4} \\ \hline 5\frac{6}{4} = 5\frac{3}{2} \end{array}$ ←—— Write a mixed numeral for $\frac{3}{2}$.

$= 5 + 1\frac{1}{2} = \mathbf{6\frac{1}{2}}$

---

34. Inventory Test

▶ Add. Write a mixed numeral in lowest terms for fractions greater than 1.

	a	b	c	d	e	f	g
1.	$\frac{5}{8}$	$\frac{3}{5}$	$\frac{2}{3}$	$\frac{5}{6}$	$\frac{5}{8}$	$\frac{2}{3}$	$\frac{6}{8}$
	$\frac{1}{8}$	$\frac{1}{5}$	$\frac{1}{3}$	$\frac{3}{6}$	$\frac{7}{8}$	$\frac{4}{3}$	$\frac{5}{8}$

	a	b	c	d	e	f	g
2.	$2\frac{1}{2}$	$4\frac{5}{8}$	$7\frac{5}{12}$	$6\frac{3}{4}$	$1\frac{5}{16}$	$2\frac{7}{8}$	$1\frac{3}{7}$
	$3\frac{1}{2}$	$2\frac{3}{8}$	$2\frac{1}{12}$	$8\frac{2}{4}$	$3\frac{7}{16}$	$3\frac{5}{8}$	$4\frac{5}{7}$

34A. Practice Set

▶ Add. Write your answers in lowest terms.

	a	b	c
1.	$\frac{3}{8} + \frac{7}{8} =$	$\frac{3}{16} + \frac{7}{16} =$	$\frac{5}{6} + \frac{4}{6} + \frac{1}{6} =$
2.	$\frac{2}{3} + \frac{2}{3} =$	$\frac{5}{12} + \frac{7}{12} + \frac{1}{12} =$	$1\frac{3}{4} + 2\frac{1}{4} + 3\frac{3}{4} =$
3.	$\frac{3}{7} + \frac{3}{7} =$	$\frac{6}{9} + \frac{4}{9} =$	$\frac{3}{11} + \frac{5}{11} + \frac{2}{11} =$
4.	$\frac{3}{4} + \frac{2}{4} =$	$\frac{4}{10} + \frac{3}{10} =$	$1\frac{7}{15} + 2\frac{1}{15} + \frac{4}{15} =$
5.	$\frac{5}{8} + \frac{2}{8} + \frac{3}{8} =$	$2\frac{1}{8} + 3\frac{5}{8} + 1\frac{7}{8} =$	$2\frac{15}{16} + 4\frac{3}{16} + 1\frac{7}{16} =$

MULTIPLES

24 is a **multiple** of 8 and 3 because $8 \times 3 = 24$.
24 is a **multiple** of 2 and 12 because $2 \times 12 = 24$.

Example: List all the whole numbers for which 16 is a multiple.

Solution: $16 = 1 \times 16$ $16 = 2 \times 8$ $16 = 4 \times 4$

Thus, 16 is a **multiple** of **1, 2, 4, 8,** and **16.**

---

35. Inventory Test

▶ List all the whole numbers for which each of the following is a multiple.

	a	b	c	d	e	f	g	h
1.	8	7	16	25	12	36	40	41
2.	15	17	64	72	80	27	3	26
3.	50	32	14	18	37	144	108	200

35A. Practice Set

▶ List all the whole numbers for which each of the following is a multiple.

	a	b	c	d	e	f	g	h
1.	35	30	20	44	6	13	9	42
2.	54	22	98	100	28	48	56	81
3.	33	29	120	125	75	60	51	288
4.	52	84	96	88	70	97	216	160

LEAST COMMON MULTIPLE

The **least common multiple (L.C.M.)** of two or more numbers is the least number that is a common multiple of the numbers.

Example: Find the L.C.M. of 3 and 8.

Solution: **1.** List multiples of 3:   3, 6, 9, 12, 15, 18, 21, **24**, . . .
2. List multiples of 8:   8, 16, **24**, 32, 40, . . .
3. Choose the <u>least</u> common multiple: L.C.M.: **24**

36. Inventory Test

▶ Find the L.C.M. of each pair of numbers.

	a	b	c	d	e	f	g
1.	2, 8	3, 9	4, 6	6, 9	12, 10	5, 7	10, 8
2.	12, 6	5, 15	8, 12	20, 4	3, 5	7, 14	16, 8
3.	20, 2	2, 5	7, 6	18, 12	48, 16	8, 20	25, 5

36A. Practice Set

▶ Find the L.C.M. of each pair of numbers.

	a	b	c	d	e	f	g
1.	5, 20	6, 8	7, 3	18, 2	15, 3	6, 10	9, 15
2.	8, 9	2, 16	12, 36	25, 15	4, 9	12, 16	30, 10
3.	18, 4	15, 6	22, 11	3, 10	5, 35	7, 9	24, 3
4.	24, 32	19, 2	4, 36	25, 125	72, 24	18, 16	16, 24

LEAST COMMON DENOMINATOR

The **least common denominator (L.C.D.)** of two or more fractions is the least common multiple of their denominators.

   You use L.C.D. to write like fractions. First you find the L.C.D. Then you write equivalent fractions having the L.C.D. as denominator.

Example: Use the L.C.D. to write like fractions for $\frac{3}{4}$ and $\frac{2}{5}$.

Solution: L.C.D.: 20

$$\frac{3}{4} = \frac{3 \times 5}{4 \times 5} \qquad \frac{2}{5} = \frac{2 \times 4}{5 \times 4}$$

$$= \frac{15}{20} \qquad\qquad = \frac{8}{20}$$

└─ Like fractions ─┘

37. Inventory Test

▶ Use the L.C.D. to write like fractions for each pair.

	a	b	c	d	e	f	g
1.	$\frac{1}{3}, \frac{1}{6}$	$\frac{1}{2}, \frac{3}{4}$	$\frac{2}{3}, \frac{1}{6}$	$\frac{5}{8}, \frac{1}{4}$	$\frac{1}{6}, \frac{3}{4}$	$\frac{1}{8}, \frac{1}{2}$	$\frac{2}{3}, \frac{1}{5}$
2.	$\frac{7}{12}, \frac{3}{4}$	$\frac{2}{3}, \frac{1}{8}$	$\frac{1}{4}, \frac{1}{3}$	$\frac{3}{7}, \frac{1}{3}$	$\frac{3}{8}, \frac{7}{16}$	$\frac{3}{4}, \frac{2}{5}$	$\frac{1}{16}, \frac{1}{3}$
3.	$\frac{3}{16}, \frac{1}{4}$	$\frac{3}{10}, \frac{2}{5}$	$\frac{5}{6}, \frac{2}{15}$	$\frac{2}{7}, \frac{1}{2}$	$\frac{3}{10}, \frac{7}{15}$	$\frac{5}{24}, \frac{3}{8}$	$\frac{7}{10}, \frac{7}{12}$

37A. Practice Set

▶ Use the L.C.D. to write like fractions for each pair.

	a	b	c	d	e	f	g
1.	$\frac{5}{8}, \frac{3}{4}$	$\frac{3}{5}, \frac{1}{2}$	$\frac{3}{4}, \frac{2}{3}$	$\frac{1}{8}, \frac{5}{6}$	$\frac{3}{10}, \frac{4}{5}$	$\frac{1}{6}, \frac{1}{4}$	$\frac{7}{8}, \frac{1}{12}$
2.	$\frac{3}{16}, \frac{1}{2}$	$\frac{7}{12}, \frac{5}{8}$	$\frac{2}{3}, \frac{7}{8}$	$\frac{5}{16}, \frac{1}{3}$	$\frac{3}{8}, \frac{4}{5}$	$\frac{2}{3}, \frac{2}{7}$	$\frac{1}{5}, \frac{7}{10}$
3.	$\frac{3}{8}, \frac{7}{32}$	$\frac{2}{5}, \frac{1}{4}$	$\frac{7}{8}, \frac{1}{10}$	$\frac{5}{24}, \frac{1}{5}$	$\frac{3}{10}, \frac{7}{100}$	$\frac{7}{8}, \frac{5}{12}$	$\frac{3}{16}, \frac{5}{8}$

Career Capsule

Machinists make and repair metal parts. A machinist has to make very accurate measurements.

▶ In Exercises **1–6,** find each length to the nearest $\frac{1}{8}$ inch.

Example:

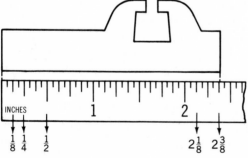

Solution: The end of the bracket is closer to $2\frac{3}{8}$ than to $2\frac{2}{8}$ or to $2\frac{4}{8}$. So the length is **$2\frac{3}{8}$ inches.**

1.

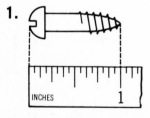

2.

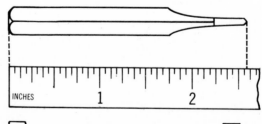

3.

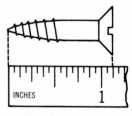

4.

5.

6.

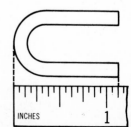

46

ADDITION—UNLIKE FRACTIONS

Unlike fractions are fractions that do not have the same denominator.

To add unlike fractions, first find the L.C.D. Write equivalent fractions having the L.C.D. as denominator. Then add.

Examples: a. $\frac{5}{8} + \frac{2}{3} = ?$ **b.** $2\frac{1}{5} + 1\frac{2}{15} = ?$

Solutions: a. L.C.D.: 24   **b.** L.C.D.: 15

$$\frac{5}{8} = \frac{15}{24} \longleftarrow \frac{5 \times 3}{8 \times 3}$$
$$+\frac{2}{3} = \frac{16}{24} \longleftarrow \frac{2 \times 8}{3 \times 8}$$
$$\overline{\frac{31}{24} = \mathbf{1\frac{7}{24}}}$$

$$2\frac{1}{5} = 2 + \frac{1}{5} = 2\frac{3}{15} \longleftarrow \frac{1 \times 3}{5 \times 3}$$
$$+1\frac{2}{15} \qquad = 1\frac{2}{15}$$
$$\overline{3\frac{5}{15} = \mathbf{3\frac{1}{3}}}$$

38. Inventory Test

▶ Add. Write your answers in lowest terms.

	a	b	c	d	e	f	g
1.	$\frac{3}{4}$ $\frac{1}{2}$	$\frac{1}{4}$ $\frac{5}{8}$	$\frac{2}{3}$ $\frac{3}{4}$	$\frac{5}{16}$ $\frac{3}{8}$	$\frac{2}{3}$ $\frac{5}{12}$	$\frac{1}{2}$ $\frac{5}{8}$	$\frac{5}{6}$ $\frac{2}{3}$
2.	$\frac{7}{8}$ $\frac{5}{16}$	$1\frac{4}{5}$ $2\frac{3}{10}$	$\frac{5}{6}$ $\frac{3}{4}$	$4\frac{1}{8}$ $2\frac{5}{16}$	$\frac{3}{10}$ $\frac{3}{4}$	$3\frac{1}{2}$ $5\frac{7}{12}$	$1\frac{13}{16}$ $7\frac{7}{8}$

38A. Practice Set

▶ Add. Write your answers in lowest terms.

	a	b	c	d	e	f	g
1.	$\frac{1}{6}$ $\frac{1}{3}$	$\frac{1}{12}$ $\frac{2}{3}$	$\frac{7}{12}$ $\frac{1}{8}$	$\frac{5}{16}$ $\frac{3}{4}$	$\frac{5}{16}$ $\frac{2}{3}$	$\frac{2}{3}$ $\frac{7}{8}$	$\frac{5}{36}$ $\frac{1}{4}$
2.	$\frac{3}{16}$ $\frac{5}{8}$	$\frac{4}{7}$ $\frac{1}{2}$	$\frac{5}{6}$ $\frac{7}{18}$	$\frac{3}{8}$ $\frac{2}{5}$	$\frac{4}{5}$ $\frac{7}{8}$	$\frac{3}{16}$ $\frac{11}{12}$	$\frac{1}{8}$ $\frac{15}{16}$
3.	$1\frac{2}{3}$ $4\frac{5}{6}$	$4\frac{3}{10}$ $2\frac{1}{5}$	$1\frac{7}{12}$ $7\frac{3}{4}$	$2\frac{1}{8}$ $1\frac{11}{16}$	$4\frac{3}{5}$ $5\frac{5}{6}$	$2\frac{7}{24}$ $7\frac{1}{3}$	$5\frac{3}{7}$ $2\frac{5}{9}$

▶ Add. Write your answers in lowest terms.

	a	b	c	d
1.	$\frac{2}{3} + \frac{1}{4} =$	$\frac{1}{4} + \frac{7}{10} =$	$\frac{1}{8} + \frac{11}{16} =$	$\frac{5}{18} + \frac{1}{6} =$
2.	$\frac{7}{16} + \frac{5}{8} =$	$\frac{7}{8} + \frac{1}{3} =$	$\frac{5}{6} + \frac{3}{4} =$	$3\frac{5}{8} + 4\frac{2}{3} =$
3.	$\frac{6}{10} + \frac{5}{8} =$	$\frac{7}{8} + \frac{5}{12} =$	$\frac{3}{8} + \frac{1}{3} =$	$1\frac{3}{4} + 7\frac{5}{7} =$

ADDITION WITH FRACTIONS—THREE ADDENDS

Examples: **a.** $\frac{2}{3} + \frac{1}{4} + \frac{7}{9} = ?$ **b.** $2\frac{1}{4} + 3\frac{5}{8} + 1\frac{2}{3} = ?$

Solutions:

a. 1. Find the L.C.D. of 3 and 4.
L.C.D. of 3 and 4: 12

2. Find the L.C.D. of 12 and 9.
L.C.D. of 12 and 9: 36
L.C.D. of 3, 4, and 9: 36

3. Add.

$$\frac{2}{3} = \frac{24}{36} \longleftarrow \frac{2 \times 12}{3 \times 12}$$
$$\frac{1}{4} = \frac{9}{36} \longleftarrow \frac{1 \times 9}{4 \times 9}$$
$$+\frac{7}{9} = \frac{28}{36} \longleftarrow \frac{7 \times 4}{9 \times 4}$$
$$\frac{61}{36} = 1\frac{25}{36}$$

b. 1. Find the L.C.D. of 4 and 8.
L.C.D. of 4 and 8: 8

2. Find the L.C.D. of 8 and 3.
L.C.D. of 8 and 3: 24
L.C.D. of 4, 8, and 3: 24

3. Add.

$$2\frac{1}{4} = 2\frac{6}{24} \longleftarrow \frac{1 \times 6}{4 \times 6}$$
$$3\frac{5}{8} = 3\frac{15}{24} \longleftarrow \frac{5 \times 3}{8 \times 3}$$
$$+1\frac{2}{3} = 1\frac{16}{24} \longleftarrow \frac{2 \times 8}{3 \times 8}$$
$$6\frac{37}{24} = 7\frac{13}{24}$$

---

39. Inventory Test

▶ Add. Write your answers in lowest terms.

	a	b	c	d	e	f	g
1.	$\frac{2}{3}$	$\frac{1}{4}$	$\frac{7}{8}$	$\frac{1}{6}$	$\frac{3}{10}$	$\frac{5}{9}$	$\frac{7}{8}$
	$\frac{5}{6}$	$\frac{3}{8}$	$\frac{3}{4}$	$\frac{3}{8}$	$\frac{1}{4}$	$\frac{1}{6}$	$\frac{5}{16}$
	$\frac{1}{2}$	$\frac{1}{2}$	$\frac{2}{3}$	$\frac{2}{3}$	$\frac{3}{5}$	$\frac{2}{3}$	$\frac{1}{4}$
2.	$\frac{2}{3}$	$\frac{8}{15}$	$\frac{1}{2}$	$\frac{3}{7}$	$1\frac{2}{3}$	$1\frac{11}{16}$	$3\frac{5}{12}$
	$\frac{5}{12}$	$\frac{1}{3}$	$\frac{2}{3}$	$\frac{5}{14}$	$2\frac{7}{8}$	$6\frac{3}{8}$	$1\frac{1}{2}$
	$\frac{5}{6}$	$\frac{4}{5}$	$\frac{3}{4}$	$\frac{1}{2}$	$3\frac{3}{4}$	$2\frac{1}{2}$	$2\frac{7}{8}$

39A. Practice Set

▶ Add. Write your answers in lowest terms.

	a	b	c	d	e	f	g
1.	$\frac{1}{6}$	$\frac{2}{5}$	$\frac{2}{3}$	$\frac{1}{2}$	$\frac{2}{3}$	$\frac{5}{8}$	$\frac{2}{3}$
	$\frac{2}{3}$	$\frac{1}{2}$	$\frac{3}{8}$	$\frac{5}{7}$	$\frac{2}{5}$	$\frac{7}{16}$	$\frac{1}{2}$
	$\frac{3}{4}$	$\frac{3}{10}$	$\frac{5}{16}$	$\frac{9}{14}$	$\frac{7}{15}$	$\frac{3}{4}$	$\frac{3}{8}$
2.	$\frac{1}{5}$	$\frac{5}{24}$	$\frac{7}{9}$	$\frac{1}{16}$	$\frac{5}{24}$	$\frac{1}{5}$	$\frac{3}{4}$
	$\frac{3}{10}$	$\frac{7}{12}$	$\frac{2}{3}$	$\frac{3}{4}$	$\frac{2}{3}$	$\frac{1}{6}$	$\frac{3}{8}$
	$\frac{2}{3}$	$\frac{1}{2}$	$\frac{5}{6}$	$\frac{7}{8}$	$\frac{7}{12}$	$\frac{1}{3}$	$\frac{5}{16}$
3.	$1\frac{3}{4}$	$4\frac{3}{5}$	$2\frac{7}{8}$	$1\frac{1}{12}$	$4\frac{2}{5}$	$4\frac{3}{16}$	$1\frac{2}{3}$
	$2\frac{1}{8}$	$1\frac{1}{2}$	$1\frac{3}{16}$	$2\frac{7}{8}$	$2\frac{2}{3}$	$8\frac{1}{2}$	$3\frac{3}{4}$
	$3\frac{1}{3}$	$2\frac{2}{3}$	$1\frac{1}{4}$	$3\frac{3}{4}$	$1\frac{7}{15}$	$2\frac{5}{12}$	$2\frac{7}{10}$
4.	$1\frac{1}{6}$	$4\frac{1}{2}$	$4\frac{2}{3}$	$1\frac{2}{3}$	$2\frac{1}{4}$	$4\frac{3}{4}$	$5\frac{7}{12}$
	$3\frac{1}{2}$	$3\frac{2}{5}$	$8\frac{3}{10}$	$2\frac{3}{4}$	$2\frac{3}{8}$	$1\frac{1}{2}$	$6\frac{1}{6}$
	$2\frac{5}{16}$	$2\frac{3}{4}$	$2\frac{1}{2}$	$2\frac{7}{12}$	$1\frac{1}{3}$	$1\frac{2}{3}$	$7\frac{3}{4}$
5.	$3\frac{1}{3}$	$2\frac{7}{8}$	$1\frac{5}{9}$	$2\frac{5}{12}$	$5\frac{7}{8}$	$3\frac{2}{3}$	$4\frac{3}{5}$
	$1\frac{5}{6}$	$3\frac{1}{4}$	$4\frac{5}{6}$	$2\frac{4}{9}$	$4\frac{1}{4}$	$1\frac{7}{15}$	$2\frac{1}{4}$
	$2\frac{1}{2}$	$4\frac{11}{16}$	$3\frac{2}{3}$	$1\frac{1}{6}$	$3\frac{1}{2}$	$2\frac{4}{5}$	$7\frac{1}{10}$

39B. Practice Set

▶ Add. Write your answers in lowest terms.

	a	b	c
1.	$\frac{3}{4} + \frac{7}{8} + \frac{1}{2} =$	$\frac{1}{7} + \frac{11}{21} + \frac{1}{3} =$	$\frac{5}{6} + \frac{7}{9} + \frac{1}{4} =$
2.	$\frac{2}{3} + \frac{5}{12} + \frac{3}{4} =$	$\frac{2}{7} + \frac{5}{21} + \frac{2}{3} =$	$\frac{4}{5} + \frac{3}{10} + \frac{7}{25} =$
3.	$\frac{7}{8} + \frac{13}{16} + \frac{1}{4} =$	$4\frac{3}{4} + 2\frac{1}{8} + 1\frac{7}{16} =$	$3\frac{2}{3} + 6\frac{1}{2} + 4\frac{7}{10} =$
4.	$\frac{5}{9} + \frac{2}{3} + \frac{1}{6} =$	$\frac{3}{8} + \frac{2}{3} + \frac{5}{16} =$	$1\frac{7}{12} + 4\frac{3}{5} + 2\frac{1}{2} =$
5.	$\frac{5}{16} + \frac{3}{8} + \frac{5}{32} =$	$1\frac{4}{5} + 6\frac{1}{3} + 2\frac{1}{4} =$	$2\frac{4}{5} + 3\frac{7}{10} + 5\frac{2}{3} =$

▶ Find the answers.

1. 8675
    296
    7038
    +4149

2. 4726
    −1937

3. 764
    × 59

4. 43)7267

5. $\frac{5}{6}$
    $+\frac{3}{8}$

6. Write in lowest terms. $\frac{24}{30} =$

7. Make the fractions equivalent. $\frac{12}{13} = \frac{}{39}$

8. Find the L.C.D. of $\frac{1}{8}$, $\frac{1}{6}$, and $\frac{2}{5}$.

9. $\frac{7}{12} + \frac{5}{8} + \frac{3}{16} =$

10. $4\frac{2}{5}$
     $3\frac{1}{2}$
     $+2\frac{5}{6}$

Stop! Repeat the Survey Test on page 43. See if you can make a perfect score.

APPLICATIONS

Transportation

▶ In Exercises **1–4,** find the total time for each trip. Use the figure at the right.

1. New York to Honolulu with a stop of $\frac{1}{3}$ hour in San Francisco.

2. Chicago to Anchorage with a stop of $\frac{1}{2}$ hour in Seattle.

3. Chicago to Flagstaff by way of Dallas and Phoenix.

4. New York to Miami with a delay of $\frac{1}{4}$ hour before landing in Miami.

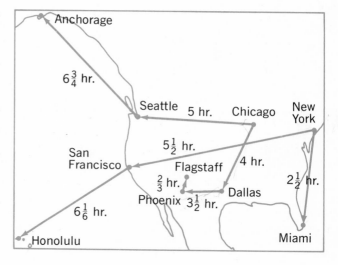

Income

A local factory keeps a record of the hours worked by part-time employees. Part of the record for one week is shown in the table at the right.

	Mon.	Tue.	Wed.	Thur.	Fri.
C. Wong	0	$4\frac{1}{4}$	0	0	$7\frac{1}{4}$
J. Norton	$3\frac{2}{5}$	0	0	$5\frac{3}{10}$	0
M. Velez	$3\frac{2}{5}$	0	$5\frac{1}{5}$	0	$2\frac{1}{10}$
B. Rosen	0	$2\frac{1}{4}$	0	$2\frac{3}{4}$	$7\frac{1}{2}$

▶ In Exercises **5–8,** find the total number of hours worked by each employee.

5. M. Velez

6. C. Wong

7. B. Rosen

8. J. Norton

9. Find the total hours worked on Tuesday by C. Wong and B. Rosen.

10. Find the total hours worked on Friday by C. Wong and M. Velez.

Subtraction with Fractions

40. Survey Test

▶ Subtract. Write your answers in lowest terms.

	a	b	c	d	e	f	g	h
1.	$\frac{3}{4}$	$\frac{9}{16}$	$\frac{5}{8}$	$\frac{3}{16}$	$\frac{2}{3}$	$\frac{5}{8}$	$\frac{9}{10}$	$\frac{11}{12}$
	$\frac{1}{4}$	$\frac{5}{16}$	$\frac{1}{2}$	$\frac{1}{8}$	$\frac{1}{4}$	$\frac{1}{6}$	$\frac{3}{4}$	$\frac{5}{8}$
2.	$\frac{9}{10}$	$\frac{3}{16}$	$2\frac{5}{8}$	$7\frac{2}{3}$	8	$9\frac{5}{16}$	$2\frac{1}{2}$	$8\frac{5}{8}$
	$\frac{2}{3}$	$\frac{1}{12}$	$1\frac{1}{3}$	$4\frac{1}{6}$	$2\frac{3}{4}$	$2\frac{7}{8}$	$\frac{2}{3}$	$2\frac{9}{10}$

3. $\frac{5}{6} - \frac{5}{8} =$　　　**4.** $\frac{7}{8} - \frac{2}{3} =$　　　**5.** $3\frac{1}{2} - 1\frac{3}{4} =$　　　**6.** $5 - 1\frac{7}{8} =$

SUBTRACTION—LIKE FRACTIONS

To subtract like fractions, subtract the numerators.
Write this difference over the denominator.

Example: $\frac{5}{8} - \frac{3}{8} = ?$　　　**Solution:**

$$\begin{array}{r} \frac{5}{8} \\ -\frac{3}{8} \\ \hline \frac{2}{8} = \frac{1}{4} \end{array} \longleftarrow \text{Lowest terms}$$

---

41. Inventory Test

▶ Subtract. Write your answers in lowest terms.

	a	b	c	d	e	f	g	h
1.	$\frac{5}{16}$	$\frac{2}{3}$	$\frac{11}{12}$	$\frac{7}{8}$	$\frac{6}{7}$	$\frac{6}{11}$	$\frac{12}{8}$	$\frac{11}{18}$
	$\frac{1}{16}$	$\frac{1}{3}$	$\frac{5}{12}$	$\frac{5}{8}$	$\frac{2}{7}$	$\frac{3}{11}$	$\frac{5}{8}$	$\frac{2}{18}$
2.	$2\frac{5}{6}$	$3\frac{9}{12}$	$2\frac{11}{16}$	$8\frac{7}{10}$	$4\frac{7}{18}$	$8\frac{4}{5}$	$4\frac{7}{12}$	$7\frac{11}{24}$
	$1\frac{1}{6}$	$1\frac{3}{12}$	$1\frac{5}{16}$	$3\frac{2}{10}$	$1\frac{1}{18}$	$6\frac{1}{5}$	$2\frac{5}{12}$	$3\frac{3}{24}$

41A. Practice Set

▶ Subtract. Write your answers in lowest terms.

	a	b	c	d
1.	$\frac{5}{12} - \frac{3}{12} =$	$\frac{11}{12} - \frac{9}{12} =$	$\frac{7}{8} - \frac{3}{8} =$	$\frac{19}{20} - \frac{3}{20} =$
2.	$\frac{9}{8} - \frac{3}{8} =$	$2\frac{7}{16} - 1\frac{3}{16} =$	$\frac{19}{32} - \frac{7}{32} =$	$4\frac{21}{24} - 1\frac{6}{24} =$

SUBTRACTION—UNLIKE FRACTIONS

To subtract fractions with unlike denominators, first find the L.C.D. of the denominators. Write equivalent fractions having the L.C.D. as denominators. Then subtract.

Examples: **a.** $\frac{5}{16} - \frac{1}{4} = ?$ **b.** $4\frac{7}{8} - 1\frac{5}{12} = ?$

Solutions: **a.** L.C.D.: 16   **b.** L.C.D.: 24

$$\frac{5}{16} = \frac{5}{16}$$
$$-\frac{1}{4} = \frac{4}{16}$$
$$\overline{\quad \frac{1}{16}}$$

$$4\frac{7}{8} = 4\frac{21}{24} \longleftarrow \frac{7\times3}{8\times3}$$
$$-1\frac{5}{12} = 1\frac{10}{24} \longleftarrow \frac{5\times2}{12\times2}$$
$$\overline{3\frac{11}{24}}$$

42. Inventory Test

▶ Subtract. Write your answers in lowest terms.

	a	b	c	d	e	f	g	h
1.	$\frac{7}{8}$	$\frac{2}{3}$	$\frac{15}{16}$	$\frac{7}{12}$	$\frac{3}{4}$	$\frac{15}{16}$	$\frac{3}{4}$	$\frac{11}{16}$
	$\frac{1}{4}$	$\frac{1}{6}$	$\frac{1}{4}$	$\frac{1}{3}$	$\frac{2}{3}$	$\frac{1}{3}$	$\frac{5}{12}$	$\frac{3}{8}$
2.	$\frac{11}{12}$	$\frac{7}{8}$	$\frac{5}{8}$	$\frac{3}{8}$	$2\frac{1}{2}$	$4\frac{3}{4}$	$1\frac{3}{5}$	$7\frac{15}{16}$
	$\frac{1}{4}$	$\frac{1}{3}$	$\frac{11}{20}$	$\frac{1}{12}$	$1\frac{1}{6}$	$2\frac{2}{5}$	$\frac{7}{16}$	$2\frac{5}{6}$

42A. Practice Set

▶ Subtract. Write your answers in lowest terms.

	a	b	c	d	e	f	g	h
1.	$\frac{3}{4}$	$\frac{7}{8}$	$\frac{1}{2}$	$\frac{19}{20}$	$\frac{15}{16}$	$\frac{7}{8}$	$\frac{2}{3}$	$\frac{3}{5}$
	$\frac{2}{5}$	$\frac{3}{16}$	$\frac{1}{3}$	$\frac{3}{5}$	$\frac{21}{32}$	$\frac{2}{3}$	$\frac{5}{16}$	$\frac{7}{12}$
2.	$\frac{3}{7}$	$\frac{7}{8}$	$\frac{15}{16}$	$\frac{7}{12}$	$\frac{4}{5}$	$\frac{9}{16}$	$\frac{9}{14}$	$\frac{11}{18}$
	$\frac{1}{3}$	$\frac{9}{16}$	$\frac{5}{6}$	$\frac{3}{8}$	$\frac{3}{4}$	$\frac{5}{32}$	$\frac{1}{2}$	$\frac{1}{9}$
3.	$3\frac{7}{8}$	$8\frac{7}{12}$	$2\frac{5}{8}$	$4\frac{13}{20}$	$7\frac{3}{5}$	$1\frac{7}{8}$	$9\frac{4}{5}$	$2\frac{5}{12}$
	$1\frac{1}{3}$	$3\frac{1}{2}$	$\frac{7}{16}$	$2\frac{2}{5}$	$2\frac{5}{12}$	$\frac{11}{16}$	$7\frac{3}{20}$	$1\frac{3}{16}$

RENAMING IN SUBTRACTION

Sometimes you have to rename before you can subtract.
In some cases, you may have to rename more than once.

Examples: a. $6 - 1\frac{1}{2} = ?$ **b.** $5\frac{1}{8} - 2\frac{2}{3} = ?$

Solutions: a. L.C.D.: 2   **b.** L.C.D.: 24

$$
\begin{array}{r}
6 = 5\frac{2}{2} \\
-1\frac{1}{2} = 1\frac{1}{2} \\
\hline
4\frac{1}{2}
\end{array}
$$

$$
\begin{array}{r}
5\frac{1}{8} = 5\frac{3}{24} = 4\frac{27}{24} \\
-2\frac{2}{3} = 2\frac{16}{24} = 2\frac{16}{24} \\
\hline
2\frac{11}{24}
\end{array}
$$

$\longleftarrow \quad 5\frac{3}{24} = 4 + \frac{24}{24} + \frac{3}{24}$

43. Inventory Test

More Challenging Exercises

▶ Subtract. Remember that you must subtract the fractions __and__ the whole numbers. Write your answers in lowest terms.

	a	b	c	d	e	f	g
1.	$5\frac{2}{3}$	$6\frac{1}{2}$	5	$7\frac{1}{2}$	$3\frac{5}{12}$	3	$1\frac{4}{9}$
	$2\frac{1}{4}$	$2\frac{1}{3}$	$2\frac{1}{4}$	$3\frac{2}{3}$	$2\frac{7}{8}$	$2\frac{7}{8}$	$\frac{5}{6}$
2.	$2\frac{5}{16}$	$3\frac{3}{8}$	$7\frac{3}{10}$	9	$7\frac{1}{2}$	$4\frac{2}{5}$	$2\frac{9}{16}$
	$1\frac{3}{8}$	$1\frac{5}{6}$	$2\frac{4}{5}$	$2\frac{7}{16}$	$2\frac{5}{16}$	$2\frac{3}{4}$	$1\frac{3}{4}$

43A. Practice Set

▶ Subtract. Remember that you must subtract the fraction __and__ the whole numbers. Write your answers in lowest terms.

	a	b	c	d	e	f	g
1.	$5\frac{1}{6}$	$2\frac{3}{8}$	4	$6\frac{2}{3}$	$2\frac{1}{5}$	$6\frac{5}{9}$	$2\frac{5}{8}$
	$2\frac{1}{3}$	$1\frac{2}{3}$	$2\frac{5}{16}$	$4\frac{3}{4}$	$1\frac{1}{4}$	$1\frac{1}{3}$	$1\frac{5}{6}$
2.	$4\frac{1}{6}$	$5\frac{1}{10}$	7	$8\frac{3}{16}$	$9\frac{7}{12}$	$2\frac{1}{2}$	$2\frac{1}{4}$
	$2\frac{3}{4}$	$2\frac{3}{5}$	$2\frac{5}{6}$	$2\frac{1}{4}$	$3\frac{1}{8}$	$1\frac{7}{8}$	$\frac{9}{16}$
3.	3	$2\frac{7}{10}$	$4\frac{3}{8}$	$4\frac{1}{2}$	7	$8\frac{2}{3}$	$6\frac{5}{8}$
	$1\frac{2}{3}$	$1\frac{1}{3}$	$2\frac{1}{2}$	$2\frac{7}{10}$	$2\frac{19}{20}$	$3\frac{4}{5}$	$2\frac{1}{3}$

▶ Find the answers.

1.
9263
806
4715
+7892

2.
4000
−3763

3.
947
×206

4.
48)7685

5.
$\frac{7}{8}$
$\frac{2}{3}$
$+\frac{9}{16}$

6. Write in lowest terms. $\frac{56}{72} =$

7.
$8\frac{5}{8}$
$-2\frac{3}{4}$

8.
12
$-6\frac{5}{6}$

9. $8\frac{5}{12} + 6\frac{3}{4} + 2\frac{5}{8} =$

10. $\frac{7}{16} - \frac{1}{3} =$

Stop! Try the Survey Test on page 51 again. See if you can make a perfect score.

APPLICATIONS

Transportation

The table at the right shows how long it takes to travel by train from New York City to five cities along the same route.

▶ In Exercises **1–6,** find how long it takes to travel between the two cities.

Example: Yonkers to Ossining

From New York City	
To	**Hours**
Yonkers	$\frac{1}{2}$
Dobbs Ferry	$\frac{2}{3}$
Ossining	1
Beacon	$1\frac{5}{6}$
Albany	$2\frac{7}{8}$

Solution:
New York City to Ossining: 1 hour
New York City to Yonkers: $-\frac{1}{2}$ hour
Yonkers to Ossining: $\frac{1}{2}$ **hour**

1. Dobbs Ferry to Ossining **2.** Yonkers to Beacon **3.** Yonkers to Albany
4. Yonkers to Dobbs Ferry **5.** Dobbs Ferry to Beacon **6.** Beacon to Albany

Graphs

The graph at the right shows the number of miles Melissa jogged over a 5-day period.

7. How many miles did she jog on Monday?

8. How many miles did she jog on Thursday?

▶ Find the difference between the number of miles she jogged on these days.

9. Thursday and Friday **10.** Tuesday and Monday
11. Friday and Tuesday **12.** Thursday and Tuesday

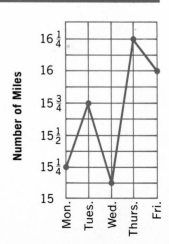

54

Multiplication with Fractions

44. Survey Test

▶ Multiply.

	a	b	c	d
1.	$\frac{1}{3} \times 7 =$	$\frac{5}{8} \times 24 =$	$\frac{2}{3} \times \frac{4}{5} =$	$\frac{5}{6} \times \frac{12}{25} =$
2.	$2\frac{4}{5} \times 1\frac{3}{7} =$	$7\frac{1}{2} \times 48 =$	$1\frac{1}{4} \times 2\frac{1}{2} =$	$25 \times \frac{7}{10} =$
3.	$1\frac{1}{8} \times \frac{2}{3} =$	$\frac{2}{3} \times \frac{1}{2} \times \frac{3}{4} =$	$1\frac{7}{8} \times 1\frac{1}{5} \times \frac{2}{3} =$	$96 \times 25\frac{5}{12} =$

FINDING THE PRODUCT

You can draw rectangles to show multiplication with fractions.

Example: $\frac{2}{3} \times \frac{3}{4} = ?$

Solution: Step 1: Show $\frac{3}{4}$. **Step 2:** Show $\frac{2}{3}$ of the $\frac{3}{4}$.

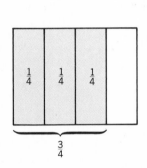

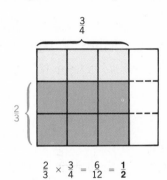

$$\frac{2}{3} \times \frac{3}{4} = \frac{6}{12} = \frac{1}{2}$$

---

45. Inventory Test

▶ Draw rectangles to help you find the products. Write your answers in lowest terms.

	a	b	c	d
1.	$\frac{2}{3} \times \frac{1}{4} =$	$\frac{3}{8} \times \frac{1}{2} =$	$\frac{5}{8} \times \frac{2}{3} =$	$\frac{3}{5} \times \frac{4}{5} =$
2.	$\frac{1}{2} \times \frac{5}{8} =$	$\frac{1}{4} \times \frac{3}{5} =$	$\frac{1}{6} \times \frac{2}{3} =$	$\frac{3}{4} \times \frac{1}{3} =$

45A. Practice Set

▶ Draw rectangles to help you find the products. Write your answers in lowest terms.

	a	b	c	d
1.	$\frac{1}{2} \times \frac{5}{6} =$	$\frac{3}{8} \times \frac{2}{3} =$	$\frac{2}{7} \times \frac{1}{4} =$	$\frac{5}{12} \times \frac{1}{2} =$
2.	$\frac{3}{4} \times \frac{4}{5} =$	$\frac{1}{6} \times \frac{3}{4} =$	$\frac{1}{8} \times \frac{1}{2} =$	$\frac{4}{5} \times \frac{2}{3} =$

MULTIPLICATION WITH FRACTIONS

To multiply with fractions, multiply the numerators. Then multiply the denominators.

Examples: a. $\frac{1}{5} \times \frac{7}{12} = ?$ **b.** $\frac{3}{4} \times \frac{8}{9} = ?$

Solutions: a. $\frac{1}{5} \times \frac{7}{12} = \frac{1 \times 7}{5 \times 12}$ **b.** $\frac{3}{4} \times \frac{8}{9} = \frac{3 \times 8}{4 \times 9}$

$= \frac{7}{60}$ $= \frac{24}{36}$ ◄——— Write in lowest terms.

$= \frac{2}{3}$

46. Inventory Test

▶ Multiply. Write your answers in lowest terms.

	a	b	c	d
1.	$\frac{2}{3} \times \frac{2}{3} =$	$\frac{7}{8} \times \frac{2}{3} =$	$\frac{1}{5} \times \frac{4}{5} =$	$\frac{3}{4} \times \frac{1}{2} =$
2.	$\frac{1}{2} \times \frac{3}{10} =$	$\frac{1}{5} \times \frac{1}{2} =$	$\frac{3}{4} \times \frac{6}{7} =$	$\frac{5}{6} \times \frac{3}{10} =$
3.	$\frac{1}{5} \times \frac{3}{8} =$	$\frac{3}{4} \times \frac{5}{8} =$	$\frac{7}{8} \times \frac{1}{6} =$	$\frac{2}{3} \times \frac{9}{16} =$
4.	$\frac{3}{4} \times \frac{4}{5} =$	$\frac{9}{10} \times \frac{2}{3} =$	$\frac{1}{5} \times \frac{3}{4} =$	$\frac{5}{12} \times \frac{3}{4} =$
5.	$\frac{5}{6} \times \frac{4}{5} =$	$\frac{5}{6} \times \frac{9}{10} =$	$\frac{15}{16} \times \frac{2}{3} =$	$\frac{5}{8} \times \frac{2}{5} =$

46A. Practice Set

▶ Multiply. Write your answers in lowest terms.

	a	b	c	d
1.	$\frac{2}{3} \times \frac{3}{5} =$	$\frac{3}{8} \times \frac{4}{7} =$	$\frac{4}{5} \times \frac{6}{7} =$	$\frac{7}{12} \times \frac{3}{14} =$
2.	$\frac{1}{4} \times \frac{8}{9} =$	$\frac{5}{6} \times \frac{3}{5} =$	$\frac{5}{8} \times \frac{10}{12} =$	$\frac{5}{12} \times \frac{9}{10} =$
3.	$\frac{1}{2} \times \frac{3}{8} =$	$\frac{7}{8} \times \frac{4}{11} =$	$\frac{1}{6} \times \frac{12}{25} =$	$\frac{11}{20} \times \frac{5}{8} =$
4.	$\frac{5}{16} \times \frac{4}{5} =$	$\frac{5}{9} \times \frac{3}{5} =$	$\frac{11}{12} \times \frac{3}{4} =$	$\frac{1}{4} \times \frac{1}{10} =$
5.	$\frac{1}{10} \times \frac{2}{3} =$	$\frac{1}{2} \times \frac{6}{10} =$	$\frac{7}{10} \times \frac{2}{3} =$	$\frac{5}{6} \times \frac{12}{25} =$

MULTIPLICATION—COMMON FACTORS

When multiplying fractions, look for a factor <u>common</u> to a numerator and a denominator. You can divide by such common factors <u>before</u> multiplying.

Examples: **a.** $\frac{5}{8} \times 12 = ?$ **b.** $\frac{8}{9} \times \frac{9}{10} = ?$

Solutions: **a.** $\frac{5}{8} \times 12 = \frac{5}{8} \times \frac{12}{1}$ **b.** $\frac{8}{9} \times \frac{9}{10} = \frac{8 \times 9}{9 \times 10}$

$$= \frac{5}{8} \times \frac{\overset{3}{\cancel{12}}}{1} \quad\quad = \frac{\overset{4}{\cancel{8}}}{\cancel{9}} \times \frac{\overset{1}{\cancel{9}}}{\cancel{10}}$$
$$\quad\; {}_{2} \quad\quad\quad\quad {}_{1} \quad {}_{5}$$

$$= \frac{5 \times 3}{2 \times 1} \quad\quad\quad = \frac{4 \times 1}{1 \times 5}$$

$$= \frac{15}{2} \quad\quad\quad\quad = \frac{4}{5}$$

$$= 7\frac{1}{2}$$

47. Inventory Test

▶ Multiply. Write your answers in lowest terms.

	a	b	c	d
1.	$\frac{2}{5} \times \frac{5}{8} =$	$\frac{4}{7} \times \frac{7}{8} =$	$\frac{7}{8} \times \frac{4}{3} =$	$\frac{2}{5} \times 25 =$
2.	$\frac{4}{5} \times 15 =$	$12 \times \frac{5}{6} =$	$\frac{3}{16} \times \frac{8}{9} =$	$\frac{21}{28} \times \frac{12}{3} =$
3.	$\frac{7}{16} \times \frac{4}{5} =$	$\frac{3}{10} \times \frac{5}{12} =$	$\frac{5}{8} \times \frac{24}{25} =$	$\frac{2}{5} \times \frac{5}{16} =$
4.	$\frac{2}{3} \times \frac{9}{10} =$	$\frac{5}{6} \times \frac{9}{10} =$	$\frac{3}{8} \times 36 =$	$18 \times \frac{3}{4} =$

47A. Practice Set

▶ Multiply. Write your answers in lowest terms.

	a	b	c	d
1.	$\frac{7}{8} \times \frac{2}{5} =$	$\frac{5}{12} \times 16 =$	$\frac{5}{12} \times \frac{4}{5} =$	$\frac{1}{5} \times \frac{3}{8} =$
2.	$\frac{8}{9} \times \frac{3}{4} =$	$\frac{2}{3} \times \frac{27}{18} =$	$\frac{7}{8} \times \frac{12}{5} =$	$\frac{5}{7} \times \frac{14}{15} =$
3.	$\frac{3}{5} \times \frac{5}{9} =$	$\frac{11}{12} \times \frac{18}{5} =$	$\frac{27}{32} \times \frac{2}{3} =$	$\frac{2}{3} \times \frac{15}{16} =$
4.	$\frac{3}{8} \times 12 =$	$\frac{3}{4} \times \frac{5}{6} =$	$20 \times \frac{3}{10} =$	$\frac{5}{16} \times 72 =$

MULTIPLICATION—MIXED NUMERALS

To multiply with mixed numerals, first write a fraction for each mixed numeral. Then multiply.

Examples: **a.** $8 \times 4\frac{2}{3} = ?$　　　　　　　**b.** $3\frac{1}{3} \times 4\frac{1}{5} = ?$

Solutions: **a.** $8 \times 4\frac{2}{3} = \frac{8}{1} \times \frac{14}{3}$　　　　　**b.** $3\frac{1}{3} \times 4\frac{1}{5} = \frac{10}{3} \times \frac{21}{5}$

$$= \frac{8 \times 14}{1 \times 3}$$

$$= \frac{\overset{2}{\cancel{10}} \times \overset{7}{\cancel{21}}}{\underset{1}{\cancel{3}} \times \underset{1}{\cancel{5}}}$$

$$= \frac{112}{3} \longleftarrow \text{Write as a mixed numeral.}$$

$$= \frac{2 \times 7}{1 \times 1}$$

$$= 37\frac{1}{3}$$

$$= \frac{14}{1} = 14$$

48. Inventory Test

▶ Multiply. Write your answers in lowest terms.

	a	b	c	d
1.	$\frac{1}{3} \times 2\frac{1}{2} =$	$1\frac{1}{6} \times \frac{3}{7} =$	$7\frac{1}{3} \times \frac{3}{8} =$	$2\frac{1}{3} \times 6\frac{1}{2} =$
2.	$1\frac{1}{4} \times \frac{3}{4} =$	$4\frac{1}{2} \times 6 =$	$\frac{3}{5} \times 1\frac{1}{4} =$	$\frac{1}{2} \times 1\frac{2}{5} =$
3.	$\frac{9}{10} \times 4\frac{1}{6} =$	$3\frac{1}{2} \times 2\frac{1}{3} =$	$2\frac{1}{3} \times \frac{3}{7} =$	$2\frac{1}{4} \times 1\frac{2}{5} =$
4.	$7\frac{1}{2} \times 2\frac{2}{5} =$	$\frac{2}{3} \times 4\frac{1}{2} =$	$3\frac{1}{3} \times 4\frac{1}{2} =$	$5\frac{5}{8} \times 3\frac{1}{5} =$

48A. Practice Set

▶ Multiply. Write your answers in lowest terms.

	a	b	c	d
1.	$1\frac{1}{6} \times 1\frac{5}{7} =$	$3\frac{3}{5} \times \frac{2}{3} =$	$\frac{1}{8} \times 3\frac{3}{4} =$	$2\frac{1}{2} \times \frac{4}{5} =$
2.	$5\frac{1}{2} \times 20 =$	$1\frac{7}{8} \times 3\frac{2}{3} =$	$3\frac{1}{5} \times 25 =$	$3\frac{1}{2} \times 4\frac{2}{3} =$
3.	$1\frac{1}{2} \times 2\frac{3}{4} =$	$1\frac{1}{4} \times 1\frac{1}{4} =$	$2\frac{1}{3} \times \frac{4}{7} =$	$28 \times 1\frac{3}{8} =$
4.	$8 \times \frac{5}{6} =$	$2\frac{1}{2} \times 12 =$	$2\frac{3}{5} \times 1\frac{1}{6} =$	$\frac{2}{3} \times 4\frac{1}{5} =$
5.	$\frac{4}{5} \times 7\frac{1}{2} =$	$4\frac{1}{2} \times 2\frac{1}{3} =$	$1\frac{1}{5} \times 4\frac{3}{8} =$	$2\frac{2}{3} \times 6\frac{3}{4} =$
6.	$3\frac{1}{8} \times 3\frac{1}{3} =$	$3\frac{1}{2} \times 2\frac{1}{4} =$	$8\frac{1}{4} \times \frac{5}{6} =$	$19 \times 1\frac{1}{2} =$

49. Inventory Test

▶ Multiply. Write your answers in lowest terms.

	a	b	c	d
1.	$18 \times 6\frac{2}{3} =$	$9\frac{3}{8} \times 72 =$	$72 \times 9\frac{1}{6} =$	$18 \times 17\frac{1}{3} =$
2.	$36 \times 12\frac{3}{4} =$	$28\frac{1}{2} \times 56 =$	$75 \times 26\frac{3}{5} =$	$85 \times 42\frac{3}{5} =$

49A. Practice Set

▶ Multiply. Write your answers in lowest terms.

	a	b	c	d
1.	$8\frac{3}{5} \times 25 =$	$48 \times 9\frac{3}{16} =$	$52 \times 9\frac{1}{4} =$	$3\frac{3}{4} \times 120 =$
2.	$7\frac{5}{8} \times 64 =$	$44 \times 12\frac{1}{4} =$	$60 \times 5\frac{7}{12} =$	$7\frac{2}{3} \times 81 =$
3.	$29\frac{1}{6} \times 42 =$	$39 \times 18\frac{1}{3} =$	$64 \times 18\frac{7}{16} =$	$29\frac{7}{8} \times 56 =$

50. Inventory Test

Multiplication—Three Factors

▶ Multiply. Write your answers in lowest terms.

	a	b	c
1.	$\frac{3}{8} \times \frac{2}{3} \times \frac{4}{5} =$	$\frac{2}{5} \times \frac{15}{16} \times \frac{4}{9} =$	$2\frac{3}{4} \times 1\frac{1}{8} \times 3\frac{5}{6} =$
2.	$\frac{3}{8} \times \frac{5}{6} \times 12 =$	$1\frac{1}{2} \times \frac{4}{5} \times 2\frac{1}{6} =$	$1\frac{1}{3} \times 3\frac{1}{5} \times 1\frac{1}{4} =$
3.	$\frac{5}{6} \times \frac{1}{4} \times \frac{2}{5} =$	$5\frac{1}{3} \times \frac{3}{4} \times 1\frac{1}{4} =$	$2\frac{1}{4} \times 2\frac{2}{3} \times 1\frac{1}{2} =$

50A. Practice Set

▶ Multiply. Write your answers in lowest terms.

	a	b	c
1.	$\frac{2}{3} \times \frac{5}{6} \times \frac{3}{5} =$	$\frac{15}{16} \times \frac{8}{9} \times \frac{3}{10} =$	$1\frac{3}{4} \times 1\frac{3}{5} \times 3\frac{1}{7} =$
2.	$\frac{5}{16} \times 4 \times \frac{7}{10} =$	$2\frac{2}{3} \times \frac{4}{5} \times \frac{5}{6} =$	$\frac{8}{15} \times \frac{5}{6} \times \frac{3}{4} =$
3.	$\frac{1}{2} \times \frac{3}{4} \times 1\frac{1}{3} =$	$\frac{3}{10} \times 3\frac{1}{8} \times 3\frac{1}{5} =$	$1\frac{5}{16} \times 2\frac{2}{3} \times 1\frac{3}{8} =$
4.	$\frac{1}{4} \times \frac{7}{8} \times 1\frac{5}{16} =$	$\frac{3}{4} \times 4\frac{1}{2} \times \frac{3}{8} =$	$\frac{1}{6} \times 3\frac{1}{5} \times 1\frac{7}{10} =$

Keeping Pace

▶ Find the answers. Write your answers in lowest terms.

1.
73,625
8,403
16,248
+83,310

2.
7025
−3819

3.
876
× 94

4.
82$\overline{)9068}$

5. $2\frac{3}{4}$
$4\frac{5}{8}$
$+2\frac{2}{3}$

6. Simplify. $\frac{28}{49} =$

7.
64
× $9\frac{3}{8}$

8. $1\frac{5}{8} \times 2\frac{2}{3} =$

9. $6\frac{5}{8} - 3\frac{3}{4} =$

10. $2\frac{1}{2} \times 2\frac{2}{7} \times \frac{7}{10} =$

Stop! Try the Survey Test on page 55 again. See if you can make a perfect score.

Career Capsule

Carpenters work in almost every kind of construction job. Carpenters use fractions in their calculations.

1. A carpenter is repairing the four legs of a stool. A piece of lumber $13\frac{3}{8}$ inches long is needed for each leg. How much is needed for four legs?

2. A carpenter wants to cut four strips, each $2\frac{3}{4}$ inches wide, from a plank. The plank is $11\frac{3}{4}$ inches wide. Can four strips be cut from the plank?

APPLICATIONS

Measurement

Volume is measured in **cubic units,** such as cubic inches, cubic feet, cubic yards, and so on. To find the volume of a **rectangular solid** such as the shoe box at the right, you use this formula.

Shoe Box

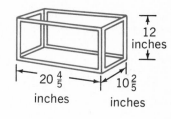

4 inches
$12\frac{2}{5}$ inches
6 inches

$$\textbf{Volume} = \textbf{Length} \times \textbf{Width} \times \textbf{Height}$$

▶ In Exercises **1–4,** find the volume.

Example: Shoe box

Solution: Volume = Length × Width × Height

$$\text{Volume} = 12\frac{2}{5} \times 6 \times 4$$

$$\text{Volume} = \frac{62}{5} \times \frac{6}{1} \times \frac{4}{1} = \frac{1488}{5} = \textbf{297}\frac{3}{5} \textbf{ cubic inches}$$

1. Storage Bin

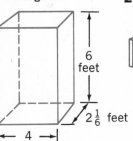

6 feet
$2\frac{1}{6}$ feet
4 feet

2. Box Car

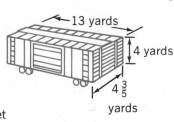

13 yards
4 yards
$4\frac{3}{5}$ yards

3. Freezer

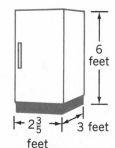

6 feet
$2\frac{3}{5}$ feet
3 feet

4. Fish Tank

12 inches
$20\frac{4}{5}$ inches
$10\frac{2}{5}$ inches

Transportation

▶ In Exercises **5–10,** find the distance traveled.

Example: Fran Ross traveled from New York to Boston in $3\frac{1}{4}$ hours at an average speed of 84 kilometers per hour.

Solution: Distance = Rate × Time

$$\text{Distance} = 84 \times 3\frac{1}{4}$$

$$\text{Distance} = 84 \times \frac{13}{4}$$

$$\text{Distance} = \textbf{273 kilometers}$$

5. Joe Osaka drove from Providence to Boston in $\frac{4}{5}$ hour at an average speed of 80 kilometers per hour.

6. Mary Jones traveled from Philadelphia to New York in $1\frac{1}{4}$ hours at an average speed of 82 kilometers per hour.

7. Leon Adams flew from New York to Washington, D.C. in $1\frac{1}{4}$ hours at an average speed of 310 kilometers per hour.

8. Ingrid Simon drove from Atlantic City to Philadelphia in $1\frac{1}{4}$ hours at an average speed of 80 kilometers per hour.

9. Luisa Kubik flew from Los Angeles to Reno in $1\frac{1}{2}$ hours at an average speed of 510 kilometers per hour.

10. Raul Vasquez drove from Detroit to Chicago in $5\frac{2}{5}$ hours at an average speed of 80 kilometers per hour.

Division with Fractions

51. Survey Test

▶ Write the reciprocal for each of the following.

	a	b	c	d	e	f	g	h
1.	$\frac{1}{3}$	$\frac{4}{6}$	$\frac{11}{5}$	21	6	$2\frac{1}{3}$	$4\frac{3}{4}$	$1\frac{5}{9}$

▶ Divide. Write your answers in lowest terms.

	a	b	c	d
2.	$8 \div \frac{1}{2} =$	$\frac{3}{4} \div 1\frac{1}{2} =$	$7\frac{1}{3} \div 1\frac{1}{3} =$	$6\frac{1}{4} \div 2\frac{1}{2} =$
3.	$\frac{3}{5} \div \frac{1}{4} =$	$\frac{7}{8} \div \frac{14}{15} =$	$1\frac{1}{6} \div \frac{7}{8} =$	$4\frac{2}{3} \div 2\frac{1}{3} =$
4.	$\frac{5}{12} \div \frac{5}{8} =$	$12 \div \frac{3}{4} =$	$2\frac{3}{4} \div 22 =$	$8\frac{3}{4} \div 6\frac{2}{3} =$

▶ Simplify each complex fraction.

	a	b	c	d	e	f	g	h
5.	$\dfrac{8}{\frac{4}{5}}$	$\dfrac{\frac{2}{3}}{12}$	$\dfrac{20}{\frac{5}{8}}$	$\dfrac{\frac{1}{4}}{7}$	$\dfrac{\frac{1}{5}}{\frac{3}{10}}$	$\dfrac{\frac{5}{8}}{2\frac{1}{8}}$	$\dfrac{4\frac{3}{8}}{2\frac{1}{2}}$	$\dfrac{1\frac{1}{4}}{3\frac{5}{12}}$

RECIPROCALS

Two numbers whose product is 1 are **reciprocals** of each other.

$\frac{5}{8} \times \frac{8}{5} = 1$ **Reciprocals:** $\frac{5}{8}$ and $\frac{8}{5}$ $7 \times \frac{1}{7} = 1$ **Reciprocals:** 7 and $\frac{1}{7}$

To write the reciprocal of a fraction, interchange its numerator and denominator.

Examples: Write the reciprocal.

        a. $\frac{7}{12}$ **b.** 9   **c.** $1\frac{1}{2}$

Solutions: a. $\frac{7}{12} \diagdown\!\!\!\diagup \frac{12}{7}$ **b.** $\frac{9}{1} \diagdown\!\!\!\diagup \frac{1}{9}$ **c.** $1\frac{1}{2} = \frac{3}{2}$ $\frac{3}{2} \diagdown\!\!\!\diagup \frac{2}{3}$

---

52. Inventory Test

▶ Give the reciprocal for each of the following.

	a	b	c	d	e	f	g	h
1.	$\frac{7}{8}$	$\frac{2}{3}$	$\frac{7}{3}$	$\frac{5}{2}$	$\frac{1}{2}$	5	$\frac{3}{10}$	$2\frac{1}{4}$
2.	$\frac{1}{3}$	7	$\frac{16}{25}$	1	$3\frac{1}{3}$	$1\frac{3}{4}$	8	$\frac{1}{20}$

52A. Practice Set

▶ Give the reciprocal for each of the following.

	a	b	c	d	e	f	g
1.	$\frac{3}{2}$	$\frac{9}{7}$	$\frac{7}{16}$	3	$\frac{1}{9}$	$1\frac{1}{4}$	$\frac{6}{7}$
2.	$\frac{9}{15}$	$3\frac{5}{8}$	$\frac{9}{5}$	$2\frac{5}{16}$	$4\frac{7}{8}$	$3\frac{1}{16}$	$1\frac{7}{8}$

DIVISION WITH FRACTIONS

To divide with fractions, multiply the dividend by the reciprocal of the divisor.

Examples: a. $\frac{7}{9} \div \frac{1}{3}$ **b.** $\frac{11}{24} \div \frac{22}{8}$

Solutions: a. $\frac{7}{9} \div \frac{1}{3} = \frac{7}{9} \times \frac{3}{1}$ **b.** $\frac{11}{24} \div \frac{22}{8} = \frac{11}{24} \times \frac{8}{22}$

$$= \frac{7}{\overset{}{\underset{3}{9}}} \times \frac{\overset{1}{3}}{1} \qquad\qquad = \frac{\overset{1}{11}}{\underset{3}{24}} \times \frac{\overset{1}{8}}{\underset{2}{22}}$$

$$= \frac{7 \times 1}{3 \times 1} \qquad\qquad\qquad = \frac{1 \times 1}{3 \times 2}$$

$$= \frac{7}{3} = 2\frac{1}{3} \qquad\qquad\qquad = \frac{1}{6}$$

---

53. Inventory Test

▶ Divide. Write your answers in lowest terms.

	a	b	c	d
1.	$\frac{3}{4} \div \frac{3}{5} =$	$12 \div \frac{4}{5} =$	$\frac{9}{10} \div 6 =$	$\frac{2}{5} \div 4 =$
2.	$5 \div \frac{1}{2} =$	$\frac{2}{5} \div \frac{4}{5} =$	$\frac{15}{16} \div 9 =$	$\frac{9}{4} \div 3 =$
3.	$\frac{4}{5} \div \frac{1}{5} =$	$\frac{5}{12} \div \frac{1}{2} =$	$\frac{1}{5} \div 2 =$	$\frac{3}{16} \div \frac{9}{4} =$
4.	$7 \div \frac{2}{3} =$	$\frac{1}{3} \div \frac{1}{9} =$	$\frac{3}{8} \div \frac{5}{16} =$	$\frac{21}{5} \div 7 =$
5.	$\frac{3}{10} \div \frac{3}{8} =$	$3 \div \frac{6}{10} =$	$\frac{11}{12} \div \frac{4}{3} =$	$\frac{7}{8} \div \frac{1}{2} =$
6.	$\frac{2}{5} \div \frac{1}{8} =$	$\frac{1}{6} \div 5 =$	$8 \div \frac{2}{3} =$	$\frac{3}{2} \div 8 =$

53A. Practice Set

▶Divide. Write your answers in lowest terms.

	a	b	c	d
1.	$\frac{1}{3} \div \frac{3}{4} =$	$\frac{7}{8} \div \frac{9}{2} =$	$\frac{7}{16} \div 7 =$	$\frac{1}{2} \div \frac{6}{5} =$
2.	$\frac{2}{5} \div \frac{4}{10} =$	$\frac{3}{4} \div \frac{1}{8} =$	$\frac{5}{9} \div \frac{1}{9} =$	$\frac{2}{3} \div \frac{5}{4} =$
3.	$15 \div \frac{3}{5} =$	$\frac{6}{16} \div 12 =$	$15 \div \frac{5}{7} =$	$\frac{3}{16} \div \frac{3}{4} =$
4.	$\frac{2}{3} \div 12 =$	$\frac{5}{6} \div \frac{1}{12} =$	$15 \div \frac{25}{4} =$	$18 \div \frac{9}{2} =$
5.	$\frac{4}{3} \div \frac{2}{3} =$	$\frac{5}{8} \div \frac{10}{3} =$	$\frac{10}{3} \div 20 =$	$\frac{6}{7} \div 12 =$
6.	$\frac{5}{16} \div \frac{5}{8} =$	$\frac{5}{16} \div \frac{10}{3} =$	$\frac{5}{6} \div \frac{5}{3} =$	$\frac{5}{8} \div \frac{15}{4} =$

DIVISION—MIXED NUMERALS

To divide with mixed numerals, first write a fraction for each mixed numeral. Then divide.

Example: $10\frac{1}{2} \div 4\frac{2}{3} = ?$

Solution: $10\frac{1}{2} \div 4\frac{2}{3} = \frac{21}{2} \div \frac{14}{3} = \frac{21}{2} \times \frac{3}{14}$

$$= \frac{\overset{3}{\cancel{21}} \times 3}{2 \times \underset{2}{\cancel{14}}} = \frac{3 \times 3}{2 \times 2} = \frac{9}{4} = \mathbf{2\frac{1}{4}}$$

---

54. Inventory Test

More Challenging Exercises

▶Divide. Write your answers in lowest terms.

	a	b	c	d
1.	$7\frac{1}{5} \div \frac{1}{5} =$	$3\frac{3}{4} \div \frac{5}{8} =$	$\frac{9}{10} \div 3\frac{3}{4} =$	$8\frac{1}{3} \div 10 =$
2.	$4\frac{3}{8} \div 5 =$	$7\frac{1}{2} \div 1\frac{1}{3} =$	$3\frac{1}{2} \div 2\frac{3}{4} =$	$15 \div 4\frac{1}{6} =$
3.	$2\frac{1}{4} \div 3 =$	$4\frac{1}{4} \div \frac{3}{4} =$	$\frac{1}{4} \div 1\frac{3}{4} =$	$1\frac{1}{3} \div 3\frac{2}{3} =$
4.	$12 \div 1\frac{1}{8} =$	$5\frac{1}{4} \div 3\frac{1}{2} =$	$5\frac{1}{10} \div 3\frac{3}{10} =$	$3\frac{3}{4} \div 2\frac{1}{2} =$
5.	$\frac{2}{3} \div 1\frac{1}{4} =$	$\frac{5}{6} \div \frac{1}{3} =$	$\frac{9}{16} \div 3\frac{3}{4} =$	$3\frac{1}{3} \div \frac{1}{6} =$
6.	$\frac{5}{6} \div 5\frac{5}{6} =$	$12 \div 2\frac{2}{5} =$	$3\frac{3}{4} \div \frac{9}{10} =$	$20 \div 3\frac{1}{3} =$

54A. Practice Set

▶ Divide. Write your answers in lowest terms.

	a	b	c	d
1.	$1\frac{1}{2} \div 2\frac{1}{2} =$	$4\frac{1}{2} \div 1\frac{1}{3} =$	$2\frac{5}{8} \div 1\frac{3}{4} =$	$\frac{3}{5} \div 3\frac{1}{3} =$
2.	$5\frac{2}{5} \div 1\frac{1}{5} =$	$4\frac{2}{3} \div 10\frac{1}{2} =$	$\frac{1}{2} \div 1\frac{1}{2} =$	$2\frac{7}{8} \div \frac{3}{4} =$
3.	$3\frac{7}{12} \div \frac{1}{2} =$	$8\frac{1}{3} \div 10 =$	$5\frac{2}{5} \div 3 =$	$4\frac{2}{5} \div \frac{1}{10} =$
4.	$1\frac{2}{5} \div \frac{1}{4} =$	$4\frac{1}{5} \div \frac{3}{10} =$	$2\frac{3}{8} \div 1\frac{5}{16} =$	$3\frac{2}{3} \div \frac{2}{3} =$
5.	$\frac{7}{12} \div 1\frac{1}{2} =$	$8\frac{3}{4} \div 6\frac{2}{3} =$	$1\frac{5}{9} \div 3\frac{1}{3} =$	$3\frac{1}{3} \div 2\frac{1}{2} =$
6.	$2\frac{2}{3} \div \frac{5}{6} =$	$\frac{9}{16} \div 1\frac{7}{8} =$	$8\frac{1}{6} \div 1\frac{1}{6} =$	$3\frac{1}{2} \div \frac{7}{8} =$

54B. Practice Set

▶ Divide. Write your answers in lowest terms.

	a	b	c	d
1.	$16 \div 2\frac{2}{3} =$	$7\frac{1}{2} \div 1\frac{1}{2} =$	$28 \div 8\frac{3}{4} =$	$\frac{7}{8} \div 6\frac{1}{4} =$
2.	$\frac{5}{8} \div \frac{15}{16} =$	$2\frac{1}{4} \div \frac{1}{8} =$	$3\frac{1}{4} \div 13 =$	$7\frac{1}{3} \div 4\frac{2}{3} =$
3.	$2\frac{3}{4} \div 1\frac{3}{4} =$	$7 \div 3\frac{1}{2} =$	$4\frac{2}{3} \div \frac{7}{9} =$	$2\frac{1}{10} \div 3\frac{3}{5} =$
4.	$6\frac{1}{8} \div 1\frac{2}{5} =$	$3\frac{5}{6} \div 1\frac{2}{3} =$	$\frac{3}{10} \div 8\frac{1}{2} =$	$3\frac{1}{2} \div 5\frac{3}{5} =$
5.	$8 \div 4\frac{4}{5} =$	$\frac{3}{5} \div 15 =$	$\frac{15}{16} \div \frac{5}{6} =$	$8\frac{1}{4} \div 1\frac{5}{6} =$

Career Capsule

Landscape architects have to be able to use fractions to compute length, circumference, and area.

▶ In Exercises **1–3,** the **circumference** (distance around) of a circular garden is given. Find the length of a path through the center of each garden.

Example: Circumference: $18\frac{6}{7}$ feet

Solution: Length of Path (Diameter) = Circumference ÷ $\frac{22}{7}$ ◀—— Fraction for π

$$= 18\frac{6}{7} \div \frac{22}{7}$$
$$= \frac{132}{7} \times \frac{7}{22}$$
$$= \frac{\overset{6}{\cancel{132}}}{\cancel{7}} \times \frac{\cancel{7}}{\cancel{22}} = \textbf{6 feet}$$

1. Circumference: $25\frac{1}{7}$ feet   **2.** Circumference: $20\frac{3}{7}$ feet   **3.** Circumference: $2\frac{1}{3}$ yards

65

COMPLEX FRACTIONS

You can write a division problem for a complex fraction.

Complex Fraction		Division Problem
$\dfrac{8}{\frac{4}{5}}$	means	$8 \div \frac{4}{5}.$
$\dfrac{\frac{7}{8}}{12}$	means	$\frac{7}{8} \div 12.$
$\dfrac{\frac{3}{4}}{\frac{1}{8}}$	means	$\frac{3}{4} \div \frac{1}{8}.$

Examples: Simplify each complex fraction.

Solutions: a. $\dfrac{8}{\frac{4}{5}} = 8 \div \frac{4}{5} = \dfrac{\overset{2}{\cancel{8}}}{1} \times \dfrac{5}{\underset{1}{\cancel{4}}} = \frac{2 \times 5}{1 \times 1} = \frac{10}{1} = \mathbf{10}$

b. $\dfrac{\frac{7}{8}}{12} = \frac{7}{8} \div \frac{12}{1} = \frac{7}{8} \times \frac{1}{12} = \frac{7 \times 1}{8 \times 12} = \mathbf{\frac{7}{96}}$

c. $\dfrac{\frac{3}{4}}{\frac{1}{8}} = \frac{3}{4} \div \frac{1}{8} = \frac{3}{4} \times \dfrac{\overset{2}{\cancel{8}}}{1} = \frac{3 \times 2}{1 \times 1} = \frac{6}{1} = \mathbf{6}$

55. Inventory Test

▶ Simplify each complex fraction.

	a	b	c	d	e	f	g
1.	$\dfrac{10}{\frac{5}{6}}$	$\dfrac{12}{\frac{2}{3}}$	$\dfrac{16}{\frac{4}{7}}$	$\dfrac{20}{\frac{4}{5}}$	$\dfrac{\frac{2}{3}}{12}$	$\dfrac{\frac{3}{5}}{9}$	$\dfrac{\frac{4}{3}}{20}$
2.	$\dfrac{14}{\frac{21}{2}}$	$\dfrac{48}{\frac{24}{7}}$	$\dfrac{9}{\frac{5}{2}}$	$\dfrac{\frac{9}{10}}{9}$	$\dfrac{\frac{3}{4}}{\frac{5}{8}}$	$\dfrac{\frac{2}{3}}{\frac{4}{5}}$	$\dfrac{\frac{15}{7}}{10}$

55A. Practice Set

▶ Simplify each complex fraction.

	a	b	c	d	e	f	g
1.	$\dfrac{18}{\frac{2}{3}}$	$\dfrac{15}{\frac{3}{8}}$	$\dfrac{\frac{5}{16}}{\frac{3}{8}}$	$\dfrac{\frac{4}{5}}{24}$	$\dfrac{\frac{3}{10}}{15}$	$\dfrac{\frac{1}{4}}{16}$	$\dfrac{\frac{7}{8}}{98}$
2.	$\dfrac{\frac{3}{5}}{\frac{3}{10}}$	$\dfrac{18}{\frac{3}{5}}$	$\dfrac{9}{\frac{1}{9}}$	$\dfrac{\frac{3}{4}}{30}$	$\dfrac{\frac{5}{16}}{\frac{3}{4}}$	$\dfrac{\frac{5}{12}}{\frac{10}{3}}$	$\dfrac{\frac{2}{3}}{\frac{5}{12}}$
3.	$\dfrac{\frac{5}{8}}{\frac{3}{16}}$	$\dfrac{28}{\frac{2}{3}}$	$\dfrac{26}{\frac{13}{2}}$	$\dfrac{\frac{2}{5}}{\frac{1}{5}}$	$\dfrac{50}{\frac{10}{13}}$	$\dfrac{\frac{2}{5}}{\frac{3}{20}}$	$\dfrac{\frac{1}{18}}{\frac{6}{5}}$

▶ Find the answers. Write your answers in lowest terms.

1.
$$76,045$$
$$8,236$$
$$41,878$$
$$+ \ 4,639$$

2.
$$806$$
$$\times \ 93$$

3.
$$8617$$
$$-4809$$

4.
$$63\overline{)7215}$$

5. $2\frac{5}{16} + 1\frac{3}{4} + 4\frac{3}{8} =$

6. $8\frac{1}{6} \times 3\frac{1}{7} =$

7. $6\frac{5}{8} - 2\frac{2}{3} =$

8. $1\frac{1}{3} \times 5\frac{1}{2} \times \frac{3}{4} =$

9. $1\frac{3}{4} \div \frac{3}{4} =$

10. $4\frac{3}{8} \div 2\frac{1}{2} =$

Stop! Try the Survey Test on page 62 again. See if you can make a perfect score.

APPLICATIONS

Food

The table at right shows the size of one serving for each type of food listed.

▶ In Exercises **1–6,** find the number of servings for each amount of food.

Example: 6 containers of yogurt

Food	Serving Size
Apple pie	$\frac{1}{8}$ pie
Canned fruit	$\frac{1}{4}$ can
Cottage Cheese	$\frac{1}{4}$ cup
Eggs	$\frac{1}{6}$ dozen
Ice cream	$\frac{1}{2}$ pint
Vegetables	$\frac{1}{4}$ package
Yogurt	$\frac{1}{2}$ container

Solution:

Number of Servings = Amount ÷ Serving Size

Number of Servings = $\quad 6 \quad \div \quad \frac{1}{2}$

Number of Servings = $\frac{6}{1} \times \frac{2}{1} = $ **12**

1. 4 cans of fruit

2. $2\frac{1}{2}$ cups of cottage cheese

3. $2\frac{1}{4}$ apple pies

4. $2\frac{2}{3}$ dozen eggs

5. $3\frac{1}{2}$ packages of vegetables

6. $2\frac{1}{4}$ pints of ice cream

Measurement

7. A plank is $1\frac{1}{2}$ feet long. How many of these planks can be cut from a board 15 feet long?

8. A stack of roofing boards is 26 inches high. Each board is $\frac{13}{16}$ inch thick. How many boards are there in the stack?

9. A plank $11\frac{1}{4}$ inches wide is to be cut lengthwise into strips $2\frac{1}{4}$ inches wide. How many strips can be cut?

10. A sheet of plastic $25\frac{1}{2}$ inches wide is to be cut into strips $2\frac{5}{8}$ inches wide. How many strips can be cut?

REVIEW OF APPLICATIONS: Fractions

▶ Choose the correct answer. Choose **a**, **b**, **c**, or **d**.

1. A plane traveled from New York to San Francisco in $5\frac{1}{2}$ hours and from San Francisco to Honolulu in $6\frac{1}{6}$ hours.
   Find the total number of hours for the trip.
   a. $11\frac{2}{3}$
   b. $12\frac{2}{3}$
   c. $11\frac{1}{2}$
   d. $11\frac{1}{3}$

2. A plane trip from New York to Miami usually takes $2\frac{1}{2}$ hours. Suppose the plane circles the airport for $\frac{3}{4}$ hour before landing.
   Find the total number of hours for the trip.
   a. $2\frac{3}{4}$
   b. $3\frac{1}{2}$
   c. $3\frac{3}{8}$
   d. $3\frac{1}{4}$

3. Laura traveled by plane from New York to Chicago in $1\frac{3}{4}$ hours, from Chicago to Seattle in 5 hours, and from Seattle to Fairbanks in $6\frac{1}{4}$ hours.
   Find the total number of hours for the trip.
   a. $12\frac{1}{4}$
   b. 13
   c. 12
   d. $12\frac{3}{4}$

4. It takes $3\frac{1}{2}$ hours to travel from Dallas to Phoenix by plane and $\frac{2}{3}$ hour to travel from Phoenix to Flagstaff by plane. Suppose there was a $1\frac{1}{2}$ hour stop in Phoenix.
   How many hours does the trip take?
   a. $5\frac{1}{6}$
   b. $5\frac{1}{3}$
   c. $5\frac{2}{3}$
   d. $4\frac{2}{3}$

The table at the right shows the number of hours that Jack worked at a part-time job over a five-week period.

▶ Use this table for Exercises **5–10**.

Name _Jack Duffy_	Dates _6/1 – 7/5_
Week	**Number of Hours**
First	$8\frac{3}{4}$
Second	$8\frac{1}{2}$
Third	$9\frac{2}{3}$
Fourth	12
Fifth	$9\frac{1}{3}$

5. Find the total number of hours that Jack worked during the first and second weeks.
   a. $16\frac{3}{4}$
   b. $17\frac{1}{4}$
   c. $16\frac{1}{4}$
   d. $17\frac{1}{2}$

6. Find the difference between the number of hours that Jack worked during the fourth and first weeks.
   a. $3\frac{1}{4}$
   b. $4\frac{1}{4}$
   c. $3\frac{3}{4}$
   d. $4\frac{3}{4}$

7. Find the total number of hours that Jack worked during the second and third weeks.
   a. $17\frac{2}{3}$
   b. $17\frac{1}{6}$
   c. $18\frac{1}{3}$
   d. $18\frac{1}{6}$

8. Find the difference between the number of hours that Jack worked during the fifth and second weeks.
   a. $1\frac{1}{6}$
   b. $\frac{1}{6}$
   c. $\frac{5}{6}$
   d. $\frac{2}{3}$

9. What was the total number of hours that Jack worked during the third, fourth, and fifth weeks?

   a. 31   **b.** 30   **c.** $30\frac{2}{3}$ **d.** $30\frac{1}{3}$

10. Find the difference between the number of hours that Jack worked during the third and first weeks.

   a. $\frac{3}{4}$ **b.** $1\frac{1}{3}$ **c.** $1\frac{1}{12}$ **d.** $\frac{11}{12}$

11. The train trip from Grand Central Terminal to Poughkeepsie takes $2\frac{1}{6}$ hours. The train trip from Grand Central Terminal to Cold Spring takes $1\frac{2}{3}$ hours.
Find the difference in hours between the two trips.

   a. $\frac{2}{3}$ **b.** $\frac{1}{2}$ **c.** $\frac{1}{6}$ **d.** $\frac{1}{3}$

The graph at the right shows the number of hours that Jerry jogged over a 5-day period.

▶ Use this graph for Exercises **12–14.**

12. How many hours did Jerry jog on Thursday?

   a. 1   **b.** $\frac{1}{2}$

   c. $1\frac{1}{4}$ **d.** $\frac{3}{4}$

13. Jerry jogged $\frac{3}{4}$ hour on Wednesday and $\frac{1}{4}$ hour on Tuesday.
Find the difference between the number of hours he jogged on Wednesday and Tuesday.

   a. 1   **b.** $1\frac{1}{4}$

   c. $\frac{1}{4}$ **d.** $\frac{1}{2}$

14. Jerry jogged $1\frac{1}{4}$ hours on Friday and $\frac{3}{4}$ hour on Wednesday. Find the difference between the number of hours he jogged on Friday and Wednesday.

   a. $\frac{1}{2}$ **b.** 2   **c.** $\frac{1}{4}$ **d.** $1\frac{1}{4}$

15. Dora budgets $\frac{1}{10}$ of her income for clothing and $\frac{1}{6}$ of her income for transportation.
How much more is budgeted for transportation?

   a. $\frac{1}{16}$ **b.** $\frac{2}{15}$ **c.** $\frac{1}{15}$ **d.** $\frac{1}{4}$

16. An average serving of ground meat is $\frac{1}{4}$ pound.
Find the number of servings in $3\frac{1}{2}$ pounds.

   a. $\frac{7}{8}$ **b.** $3\frac{3}{4}$ **c.** 14   **d.** $\frac{1}{14}$

17. One serving of chocolate cake is $\frac{1}{12}$ cake.
Find the number of servings in $2\frac{1}{4}$ cakes.

   a. 18   **b.** $5\frac{1}{3}$ **c.** 27   **d.** 30

18. Stacy allows $\frac{1}{4}$ pound of fresh asparagus per serving.
How many servings will she get from $2\frac{1}{4}$ pounds?

   a. $1\frac{7}{16}$ **b.** $\frac{9}{16}$ **c.** 5   **d.** 9

► In Exercises **19–20,** use the formula:

Distance = Rate × Time

19. Margaret drove from New York to Philadelphia in $1\frac{1}{8}$ hours at an average of 80 kilometers per hour.
How many kilometers did she drive?

  a. $89\frac{1}{8}$ **b.** $78\frac{2}{9}$ **c.** 90   **d.** $90\frac{1}{8}$

20. A plane went from Washington, D.C. to Augusta in $2\frac{1}{3}$ hours at 318 kilometers per hour.
Find the number of kilometers traveled.

  a. 636   **b.** $136\frac{2}{7}$ **c.** $320\frac{1}{3}$ **d.** 742

► In Exercises **21–22,** use the formula:

Rate = Distance ÷ Time

21. A family drove 60 miles in $1\frac{1}{4}$ hours.
Find their average rate of speed in miles per hour.

  a. 65   **b.** 48   **c.** 75   **d.** 55

22. A plane traveled 660 miles in $1\frac{1}{2}$ hours.
Find the rate in miles per hour.

  a. 940   **b.** 990   **c.** 330   **d.** 440

23. A plank of wood $22\frac{3}{4}$ inches long is to be cut lengthwise into $3\frac{1}{4}$ inch strips.
How many strips can be cut from the plank?

  a. 7   **b.** $6\frac{10}{13}$ **c.** 8   **d.** 9

► In Exercises **24–26,** use the formula:

Volume = Length × Width × Height

24. A tool box is $1\frac{1}{4}$ feet long, $\frac{3}{4}$ foot wide, and $\frac{2}{3}$ foot high.
Find the volume of the tool box in cubic feet.

  a. $\frac{5}{16}$ **b.** $\frac{5}{8}$

  c. $\frac{15}{16}$ **d.** $2\frac{2}{3}$

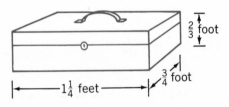

25. A tote bag is 12 inches long, $3\frac{1}{3}$ inches wide, and $8\frac{1}{4}$ inches high.
Find its volume in cubic inches.

  a. 330   **b.** $23\frac{7}{12}$

  c. 1320   **d.** 990

26. A cabinet is 2 feet long, $1\frac{1}{2}$ feet wide, and $4\frac{2}{3}$ feet high.
Find its volume in cubic feet.

  a. $7\frac{1}{3}$ **b.** 28

  c. 14   **d.** 7

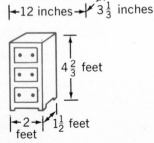

REVIEW OF SKILLS: Whole Numbers and Fractions

▶ Complete this puzzle. Write the answers to the exercises in the boxes of the puzzle. The answers should check across and down. Each box holds one digit.

ACROSS

1. $26 + 48 + 72 + 28 =$ ___

3. $81 \div \frac{1}{6} =$ ___

6. L.C.D. for $\frac{5}{7}$ and $\frac{2}{9}$ is ___

7. $29 \times 23 =$ ___

9. $5\frac{5}{6} \times 18 =$ ___

11. $16 \times 1\frac{1}{2} =$ ___

12. $15\frac{3}{4} - 3\frac{9}{12} =$ ___

13. $22 \div \frac{2}{5} =$ ___

14. $58 + 119 + 199 =$ ___

17. $2\frac{5}{12} + 5\frac{1}{2} + 6\frac{1}{4} + 8\frac{5}{6} =$ ___

18. $8\frac{2}{5} \times 1\frac{2}{3} =$ ___

19. $474\overline{)48,348} =$ ___

21. $27 \times 36 =$ ___

24. $3\frac{3}{5} \times 3\frac{1}{3} =$ ___

26. $12\frac{1}{2} \div \frac{1}{4} =$ ___

27. $64 \times 15 =$ ___

29. $18\frac{1}{3} - 3\frac{6}{18} =$ ___

30. $2688 \div 48 =$ ___

31. $32 \times 3\frac{1}{2} =$ ___

32. $44 \times 5\frac{1}{2} \times \frac{1}{2} =$ ___

DOWN

1. $32\overline{)416} =$ ___

2. $4302 - 3838 =$ ___

4. $3 \times 3 \times 3 \times 3 =$ ___

5. $276 + 329 =$ ___

6. $67 \times 9 =$ ___

8. $18 + 26 + 27 =$ ___

10. $48 \times 11\frac{1}{2} =$ ___

11. $11,309 \div 43 =$ ___

15. $45 \times 160 =$ ___

16. $10,764 - 2635 =$ ___

19. $43 + 38 + 28 =$ ___

20. $713 + 199 + 825 + 364 =$ ___

22. $13,091 - 5530 =$ ___

23. $2\frac{1}{2} \div \frac{1}{8} =$ ___

25. $15\overline{)1425} =$ ___

28. $18\frac{3}{5} + 25\frac{1}{2} + 16\frac{9}{10} =$ ___

30. $6\frac{1}{2} \times 8 =$ ___

Decimals

56. Survey Test

1. Write in words.

   a .28   b .048   c 3.7   d 82,795   e 2,500,000

2. Write in decimals.

   a Twenty-five and seven hundredths   b Two hundred five thousandths

3. Arrange in order of size, beginning with the least.

   a .832, .83, .9   b 7.15, .715, 71.5   c .02, .2, .003

THE DECIMAL SYSTEM OF NUMERATION

The system of numeration that you use has a **base of ten** and is called the **decimal system.** The value of any place is ten times the value of the place to the right of it, as shown below.

Millions	Hundred thousands	Ten thousands	Thousands	Hundreds	Tens	Units	and	Tenths	Hundredths	Thousandths	Ten-thousandths	Hundred-thousandths
1,	5	2	8,	7	3	4	.	5	6	9	7	2

When you write decimals, you use a point to locate the ones, or units place in the numeral. When you read a number named by a decimal, read first the part of the numeral at the left of the point and then the part at the right. The word "and" is used to show the position of the decimal point.

Examples: Use words to name each decimal.

    a. .4   **b.** 7.02   **c.** 372.255   **d.** 1.0007

Solutions: **a.** Four tenths

       b. Seven <u>and</u> two hundredths

       c. Three hundred seventy-two <u>and</u> two hundred fifty-five thousandths

       d. One <u>and</u> seven ten-thousandths

---

57. Inventory Test

Using Words to Write Decimals

▶ Write in words.

	a	b	c	d	e
1.	.4	386	12,324	658,302	.2793
2.	.38	.262	6.271	48,900	80.008
3.	.02	48.5	.078	276.37	42,631
4.	76.4	.75	.269	.9264	.7205
5.	.18	.025	48.17	100,000	5,857,200

57A. Practice Set

▶ Write in words.

	a	b	c	d	e
1.	.461	29,368	80,006	785,000	.0045
2.	3.72	17.63	3000	2.43	8,600,060
3.	.8	.894	.0527	27.83	368.273
4.	920	.003	48,940	.065	.5623
5.	4.78	9.707	.2121	1.001	9.5623

58. Inventory Test

Writing Decimals

▶ Write a decimal for each of the following.

	a	b
1.	Seven tenths	Forty-six thousand, ninety
2.	Twelve thousand	Thirty-five thousandths
3.	Twelve thousandths	Two hundred five ten-thousandths
4.	Eight and sixteen hundredths	Eight million, forty
5.	Three thousand, two hundred five	Six and two hundredths

58A. Practice Set

▶ Write a decimal for each of the following.

	a	b
1.	Eight thousandths	Five ten-thousandths
2.	Two million, five hundred thousand	Twenty-eight thousand, two
3.	One hundred and one hundredth	Ten and fifty thousandths
4.	One hundred sixty-two thousandths	Nine hundred sixteen ten-thousandths
5.	Eighteen ten-thousandths	Fifty million, thirty thousand
6.	Two hundred eighty-five thousand	Four hundred-thousandths

COMPARING DECIMALS

Decimals are easy to compare when they have the same number of decimal places.

Example: Arrange .3, .33, and .325 in order from least to greatest.

Solution: Annex zeros when necessary so that the decimals have the <u>same</u> number of places. Annexing zeros does not change the value of the decimal.

.3 = .300   .33 = .330   .325 = .325

Now arrange the decimals in order. Start with the least.
.300   .325   .330

59. Inventory Test

▶ Arrange in order, beginning with the least.

	a	b	c
1.	.6, .065, .63	.04, .05, .048	.4956, .49, .5
2.	.481, .5, .52	.58, 2, .575	.2, .024, .02
3.	.2, .222, .22	.3, .31, .303	.6, .666, .66
4.	.2, .25, .026	.62, .6319, .633	.72, .7, .762
5.	.81, .8, .8321	8.4, .85, .848	.46, .063, .36

59A. Practice Set

▶ Arrange in order, beginning with the least.

	a	b	c
1.	.083, .83, .8	2.5, 25, .25	.027, 2.7, .2702
2.	.908, .994, .959	.426, .48, .482	.008, .07, .08
3.	7.2, 7, 7.12	.05, .051, .04	1, .185, .01
4.	.25, .2, .025	.56, 1, .561	6.3, 6.274, 6.36
5.	.96, .956, 9.6	.91, .9, .923	10.0011, .10, .11
6.	8.5, .85, .085	.0401, .042, .4	.3, .32, .33
7.	.02, .009, .1	.03, .045, .0054	.3, .097, .0938

▶ Find each answer. Write fractions in lowest terms.

1.	2.	3.	4.
87,294	58,275	803	
6,805	−21,832	× 76	59)2832
61,279			
+ 4,338			

5. $7\frac{3}{16} + 2\frac{1}{2} + 4\frac{7}{8} =$

6. $8 - 2\frac{7}{12} =$

7. $24 \times 16\frac{2}{3} =$

8. Rename. $\frac{3}{8} = \frac{}{72}$

9. Arrange in order. Begin with the least.
.61, .623, .064

10. Susan Chin drove 162 miles the first week in February, 94 miles the second week, 116 miles the third week, and 58 miles the fourth week.
Find the average number of miles per week Susan drove in February.

Stop! Try the Survey Test on page 72 again. See if you can make a perfect score.

Career Capsule

Home economists carefully regulate cooking temperatures in order to preserve the nutritional values of food and to obtain the best results.

▶ Match the cooking temperatures in Exercises **1–8** with the temperatures indicated on the scale at the right. Answer A, B, C, D, and so on.

1. Water freezes: 0°

2. Water simmers: 46°

3. Water boils: 100°

4. Slow oven: 131°

5. Moderate oven: 177°

6. Hot oven: 232°

7. Temperature for deep-fat frying: 190°

8. Temperature for broiling: 288°

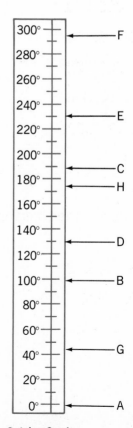

Celsius Scale

Addition and Subtraction with Decimals

60. Survey Test

▶ Add or subtract as indicated.

	a	b	c	d	e	f
1.	2.34 .76 1.08 + .96	27.6 9.8 12.3 + 6.5	.432 .704 .916 +.829	1.639 .028 9.124 +8.796	963.8 72.4 100.9 + 84.5	12.08 .17 8.83 + 9.25
2.	27.3 − 9.5	.283 −.105	1.673 − .938	286.4 −109.9	7.35 −3.85	2.000 − .763

	a	b	c
3.	7.23 + 8.65 + 10.62 =	8.27 − 4.18 =	25.736 + 17.092 =
4.	19.5 + 10.3 + 6.8 =	12.627 − 8.301 =	2765.2 − 1823.7 =

ADDITION WITH DECIMALS

To add with decimals, line up the decimal points one under the other.
Then add as with whole numbers.

Example: 7.14 + 16.75 + 7.6 + 32.65 = ?

Solution: Line up the decimal points.

$$
\begin{array}{r}
\overset{2\ \ 2\ \ 1}{7.14} \\
16.75 \\
7.6 \\
+32.65 \\
\hline
64.14
\end{array}
$$

---

61. Inventory Test

▶ Add.

	a	b	c	d	e	f	g
1.	3.6 4.2 5.1 3.7	15.6 7.8 10.3 .8	12.9 17.3 8.2 6.9	20.4 7.6 19.8 10.3	2.63 1.75 .48 1.03	29.3 82.1 17.4 9.8	23.62 1.85 .96 40.72
2.	9.6 8.7 4.4 7.3 8.2	4.3 8.9 2.3 .4 1.6	21.3 8.1 19.6 7.4 .9	32.7 19.3 8.2 6.8 46.5	.732 .901 .316 .217 .185	12.65 8.09 7.16 48.03 9.17	1.186 .735 9.026 .394 2.846

61A. Practice Set

▶ Add.

	a	b	c	d	e	f	g
1.	3.67	.183	26.21	.463	8.173	46.48	5.270
	12.55	1.976	17.38	.173	4.068	1.92	2.448
	8.19	8.029	1.92	.902	3.948	12.75	.693
	5.67	.338	40.68	.784	.733	8.69	1.027
2.	.273	82.5	27.38	.7826	83.75	100.3	1.732
	8.604	168.3	9.42	.4072	9.64	87.5	2.085
	1.448	97.9	18.78	.2457	27.08	125.8	.993
	.325	192.8	3.02	.5621	12.38	93.4	.036
	1.174	26.1	9.35	.1074	4.13	186.8	8.186

SUBTRACTION WITH DECIMALS

To subtract with decimals, line up the decimal points one under the other. Then subtract as with whole numbers.

Example: 3.573 − .298 = ? Check your answer.

Solution:

$$
\begin{array}{r}
\overset{4\ \ 6\ \ 13}{3.\cancel{5}\cancel{7}\cancel{3}} \\
- \quad .298 \\
\hline
3.275
\end{array}
$$

Check:

$$
\begin{array}{r}
3.275 \\
+ \ .298 \\
\hline
3.573
\end{array}
$$

---

62. Inventory Test

Subtraction with Decimals

▶ Subtract. Check your answers.

	a	b	c	d	e	f	g
1.	7.32	2.75	1.17	3.85	9.64	27.3	.732
	1.08	.68	.92	1.75	7.15	18.9	.651
2.	.803	7.17	9.00	.362	6.85	18.5	6.273
	.411	2.08	1.75	.177	1.28	7.9	.192
3.	12.35	1.00	6.152	98.6	80.3	5.276	5.251
	8.47	.78	4.071	45.8	71.5	3.298	2.738

62A. Practice Set

▶ Subtract. Check your answers.

	a	b	c
1.	9.3 − 7.2 =	18.5 − 9.7 =	1.73 − .99 =
2.	83.5 − 76.7 =	10.8 − 2.5 =	2.00 − 1.75 =
3.	9.72 − 4.38 =	1.752 − .888 =	183.5 − 176.9 =
4.	5.88 − 2.92 =	20.3 − 7.9 =	76.7 − 62.5 =
5.	12.1 − 9.5 =	176.6 − 85.9 =	98.2 − 17.4 =

62B. Practice Set

▶ Add or subtract as indicated.

a	b
1. 2.5 + 3.8 + 1.6 =	23.62 + 48.05 + 26.37 =
2. 12.9 + 7.2 + 10.3 =	8.3 + 19.9 + 20.7 + 5.5 =
3. 18.32 − 6.48 =	20.273 − 8.144 =
4. .123 + .627 + 1.836 =	8.035 + 2.737 − 4.732 =
5. 263.7 − 145.3 =	2463.75 − 903.28 =
6. 18.3 + 7.4 − 12.6 =	20.25 − 8.63 − 4.92 =
7. 9.27 − 4.63 + 5.24 =	.763 − .248 + 3.259 =

Keeping Pace

▶ Find the answers.

1.
$$\begin{array}{r} 84{,}276 \\ 9{,}403 \\ 12{,}684 \\ +26{,}325 \\ \hline \end{array}$$

2.
$$\begin{array}{r} 173 \\ \times\ 94 \\ \hline \end{array}$$

3.
$$\begin{array}{r} 4263 \\ -3182 \\ \hline \end{array}$$

4. $38\overline{)3914}$

5.
$$\begin{array}{r} 48 \\ \times\ 9\frac{2}{3} \\ \hline \end{array}$$

6. $\frac{5}{16} + \frac{2}{3} + \frac{1}{4} =$

7. $7\frac{1}{2} - 3\frac{5}{8} =$

8.
$$\begin{array}{r} 27.308 \\ 2.114 \\ .679 \\ .030 \\ +30.895 \\ \hline \end{array}$$

9.
$$\begin{array}{r} 293.8 \\ -146.9 \\ \hline \end{array}$$

10. a   7.25 + 9.61 + 12.78 = ___

   b   3984.3 − 2197.8 = ___

Stop!   Try the Survey Test on page 76 again. See if you can make a perfect score.

APPLICATIONS

Banking ───────────────────────────

When a deposit is made in a checking account and when a check is written, you must fill out the check stub. This tells you how much money is in your account. The amount of money in the account is the **balance carried forward.**

▶ In Exercises **1–6,** find the balance carried forward (BAL CAR'D FOR'D).

Example:

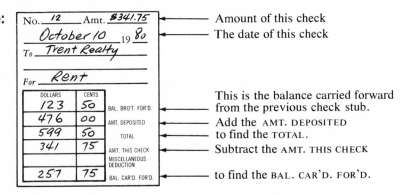

No. 12 Amt. $341.75	
October 10 19 80	Amount of this check
To Trent Realty	The date of this check
For Rent	

DOLLARS	CENTS	
123	50	BAL. BRO'T. FOR'D.
476	00	AMT. DEPOSITED
599	50	TOTAL
341	75	AMT. THIS CHECK
		MISCELLANEOUS DEDUCTION
257	75	BAL. CAR'D. FOR'D.

- Amount of this check
- The date of this check
- This is the balance carried forward from the previous check stub.
- Add the AMT. DEPOSITED to find the TOTAL.
- Subtract the AMT. THIS CHECK
- to find the BAL. CAR'D. FOR'D.

1.

No. 6   Amt. $28.15
March 14   19 __
To Center Utility
For Gas

DOLLARS	CENTS	
11	25	BAL. BRO'T. FOR'D.
105	00	AMT. DEPOSITED
116	25	TOTAL
28	15	AMT. THIS CHECK
		MISCELLANEOUS DEDUCTION
		BAL. CAR'D. FOR'D.

2.

No. 42   Amt. $115.90
December 3   19 __
To Tomson Garage
For Car Repairs

DOLLARS	CENTS	
209	35	BAL. BRO'T. FOR'D.
50	00	AMT. DEPOSITED
259	35	TOTAL
115	90	AMT. THIS CHECK
		MISCELLANEOUS DEDUCTION
		BAL. CAR'D. FOR'D.

3.

No. 86   Amt. $43.20
July 17   19 __
To Plaza Stationery
For Books, cards

DOLLARS	CENTS	
202	21	BAL. BRO'T. FOR'D.
—	—	AMT. DEPOSITED
202	21	TOTAL
43	20	AMT. THIS CHECK
		MISCELLANEOUS DEDUCTION
		BAL. CAR'D. FOR'D.

4.

No. 7   Amt. $12.90
September 2   19 __
To Pete's Barber
For Cut

DOLLARS	CENTS	
75	80	BAL. BRO'T. FOR'D.
321	60	AMT. DEPOSITED
397	40	TOTAL
12	90	AMT. THIS CHECK
		MISCELLANEOUS DEDUCTION
		BAL. CAR'D. FOR'D.

5.

No. 18   Amt. $23.60
April 21   19 __
To Joe's Diner
For Lunches

DOLLARS	CENTS	
—	—	BAL. BRO'T. FOR'D.
200	00	AMT. DEPOSITED
200	00	TOTAL
23	60	AMT. THIS CHECK
		MISCELLANEOUS DEDUCTION
		BAL. CAR'D. FOR'D.

6.

No. 36   Amt. $325.80
February 29   19 __
To Foster Management
For Rent

DOLLARS	CENTS	
—	—	BAL. BRO'T. FOR'D.
700	00	AMT. DEPOSITED
700	00	TOTAL
325	80	AMT. THIS CHECK
		MISCELLANEOUS DEDUCTION
		BAL. CAR'D. FOR'D.

7. Jim had a balance of $92.17 in his checking account. He deposited two $5 bills, one $50 bill and a check for $10.50.
Find his new balance.

8. Sandra counted her money. She had 7 one dollar bills, 8 ten dollar bills and 20 nickels. She spent $40.00 and deposited the rest.
How much did she deposit?

Multiplication with Decimals

63. Survey Test

▶ Multiply.

	a	b	c	d	e	f	g
1.	.8 3	.09 6	3.5 7	.25 36	.275 4	.286 .01	3.5 48
2.	19.3 4.8	.063 .04	200 .045	8.6 3.5	.026 .9	9.63 .52	30.5 1.2

MULTIPLICATION—DECIMALS AND WHOLE NUMBERS

To multiply a decimal and a whole number, first multiply as with whole numbers. Then place the decimal point in the product. The number of decimal places in the product equals the sum of the decimal places in the factors. (Each place to the right of the decimal point is a **decimal place.**)

Examples: a. $7.45 \times 5 = ?$ **b.** $.087 \times 43 = ?$

Solutions: a.

		Decimal Places
7.45	⟵	2
× 5	⟵	0
37.25	⟵	2 + 0 = 2

b.

		Decimal Places
.087	⟵	3
× 43	⟵	0
261		
3480		
3.741	⟵	3 + 0 = 3

---

64. Inventory Test

▶ Multiply.

	a	b	c	d	e	f	g	h
1.	2.6 8	8.5 7	.92 9	36.2 4	20.5 6	.316 9	4.28 3	9.17 5
2.	.067 7	1.26 12	3.4 26	.72 80	6.2 15	.9 53	18.6 29	2.75 18
3.	3.27 46	.029 83	9.06 74	2.16 19	.123 86	6.59 78	28.3 64	.008 27

64A. Practice Set

▶ Multiply.

	a	b	c	d	e	f	g	h
1.	12.3 8	.29 32	4.7 35	.17 23	2.89 12	.016 15	7.03 14	8.2 72
2.	.48 62	8.4 193	4.36 47	.172 25	.69 88	.155 10	.45 430	6.57 28
3.	27.5 63	8.9 82	.006 54	.09 375	1.73 96	10.0 271	19.2 19	26.34 83

MULTIPLICATION WITH DECIMALS

To multiply with decimals, first multiply as with whole numbers. Then place the decimal point correctly in the product.

Examples: a. $.8 \times .3 = ?$ **b.** $2.7 \times 1.25 = ?$

Decimal Places   Decimal Places

Solutions: a.

$$\begin{array}{r} .8 \longleftarrow 1 \\ \times .3 \longleftarrow 1 \\ \hline .24 \longleftarrow 1+1=2 \end{array}$$

b.

$$\begin{array}{r} 2.7 \longleftarrow 1 \\ \times 1.25 \longleftarrow 2 \\ \hline 135 \\ 540 \\ 2700 \\ \hline 3.375 \longleftarrow 1+2=3 \end{array}$$

---

65. Inventory Test

▶ Multiply.

	a	b	c	d	e	f	g
1.	9.2 .3	6.8 .4	.27 .8	2.4 .13	.72 2.8	.66 .25	1.7 1.8
2.	.91 6.2	.29 1.2	1.08 .2	2.65 1.5	240 .05	.8 2.6	.125 3.2
3.	.87 .19	6.2 .18	7.3 3.8	4.24 .07	.042 60	2.8 9	27 .088

65A. Practice Set

▶ Multiply. Check the position of the decimal point carefully each time.

	a	b	c	d	e	f	g
1.	2.8 1.5	.32 2.5	18.6 .3	100 .35	.72 3.4	5.6 10.2	.5 2.8
2.	13.8 3.9	.076 24	2.05 1.7	.95 .76	.168 2.1	84.3 1.2	3.1 .167
3.	.429 7.5	.063 100	96 .2	1.79 .33	2.5 26	40.1 .9	600 .028
4.	53.7 6.4	.44 39	7.2 4.8	26 .045	300 6.2	16.9 .7	55.8 .17

INSERTING ZEROS

When placing the decimal point in a product, you sometimes have to insert zeros.

Examples: a. $.13 \times .5 = ?$ **b.** $.25 \times .03 = ?$

Decimal Places

Solutions: a.

$$\begin{array}{r} .13 \\ \times\ .5 \\ \hline .065 \end{array}$$

⟵ 2
⟵ 1
⟵ 2 + 1 = 3

b.

$$\begin{array}{r} .25 \\ \times .03 \\ \hline .0075 \end{array}$$

⟵ 2
⟵ 2
⟵ 2 + 2 = 4

---

66. Inventory Test

More Challenging Exercises

▶ Multiply. Check that you have placed all decimal points correctly.

	a	b	c	d	e	f	g
1.	.35 .13	.32 .6	1.8 .05	.392 1.5	300 .04	.045 .02	.16 .16
2.	2.3 .016	.075 4.6	88 1.1	.013 .5	1.3 .027	7.4 .8	500 .073

66A. Practice Set

▶ Multiply.

	a	b	c	d	e	f	g
1.	.603 .4	28 .27	.036 .03	.25 .12	9.26 1.3	.018 .02	.635 .8
2.	38.2 1.9	.025 .25	3.5 .018	200 1.25	3.14 .006	.009 .08	2.86 3.9
3.	3.721 25	.012 .06	.043 3.3	28.3 2.9	.013 1.4	65 .041	.201 2.1
4.	2000 .025	.964 .07	1.72 7.5	.385 62	5000 .017	90 .023	17.2 .25

Keeping Pace

▶ Find the answers. Write fractions in lowest terms.

1. 18,265
       7,618
       90,269
     + 4,614

2.   623
       × 95

3. 67)5025

4. $8\frac{1}{2} + 2\frac{2}{3} + 3\frac{4}{5} =$

5. $4\frac{4}{5} \times \frac{5}{16} =$

6.   3.000
       −1.651

7.   92
       ×$18\frac{3}{4}$

8.   12.3
       ×.063

9. Write in words. 6.035

10. John bought 45 baby chicks for $7.50. The expenses of raising them for market amounted to $45. He lost 5 chicks but sold the others for $1.75 each. How much profit did he make?

Stop! Try the Survey Test on page 80 again. See if you can make a perfect score.

Career Capsule

Toll booth clerks collect tolls on highways and bridges. They must be able to make change quickly and accurately.

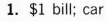

The toll on a highway is 35¢ per car (two-axle vehicle) and 40¢ per axle for all other vehicles.

In Exercises **1–4**, how much change should the driver receive?

1. $1 bill; car

2. $5 bill; 3 axles

3. $10 bill; car

4. $20 bill; 4 axles

APPLICATIONS

Clothing

The amount and cost of the cloth needed to make each item in Exercises **1–4** are given.

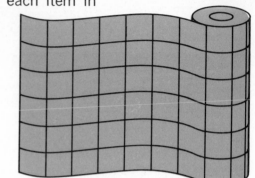

▶ Find the cost of the cloth needed for each item.

1. Shirt: 2.5 meters at $3.00 per meter

2. Slacks: 2.5 meters at $3.20 per meter

3. Skirt: 1.5 meters at $3.50 per meter

4. Jacket: 2.75 meters at $4.00 per meter

Housing

The cost of electricity depends on the number of **kilowatts** used per hour. This is called **kilowatt hours** (abbreviated: kwh).

▶ In Exercises **5–8,** find the yearly cost of each appliance if electricity costs $.086 per kilowatt hour.

5. Washing machine: 100 kwh per year

6. Clothes dryer: 1000 kwh per year

7. Color TV: 700 kwh per year

8. Range/oven: 1300 kwh per year

Measurement

To save money and energy, an air conditioner should be the right size for the room in which it is used. The right size depends on the volume of the room. Volume is measured in **cubic units.** You can use this formula to find the volume of a rectangular solid, such as a room.

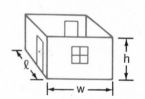

$$\textbf{Volume} = \textbf{Length} \times \textbf{Width} \times \textbf{Height}$$

▶ Find the volume of each room in Exercises **9–13.**

Example: Length: 3 meters
Width: 4 meters
Height: 2.5 meters

Solution: Volume = Length × Width × Height

Volume = 3 × 4 × 2.5
Volume = **30 cubic meters**

9. Length: 4 meters; Width: 4 meters; Height: 2.5 meters

10. Length: 6.4 meters; Width: 5 meters; Height: 2.5 meters

11. Length: 5 meters; Width: 5.2 meters; Height: 3 meters

12. Length: 5.5 meters; Width: 6 meters; Height: 3 meters

13. Length: 5 meters; Width: 4 meters; Height: 2.5 meters

Division with Decimals

67. Survey Test

▶ Divide.

	a	b	c	d	e
1.	4)2.4	9).27	7)25.9	8)2.608	.6).126
2.	.5)865	2.2)1.386	.17).816	.008).184	9.1).03822

▶ Divide. Round each quotient to the nearest tenth.

	a	b	c	d	e
3.	.02)1.25	.8)2.53	3)7	6).947	4.9)3.080

DIVIDING A DECIMAL BY A WHOLE NUMBER

To divide a decimal by a whole number, divide as for whole numbers. Place the decimal point in the quotient directly above the decimal point in the dividend.

Example: 210.4 ÷ 8 = ?   Check your answer.

$$\begin{array}{r} 26.3 \\ 8\overline{)210.4} \end{array}$$

Solution: 8)210.4

Check:
$$\begin{array}{r} 26.3 \\ \times\ \ 8 \\ \hline 210.4 \end{array}$$

---

68. Inventory Test

▶ Divide. Check your answers.

	a	b	c	d	e	f
1.	2)21.6	8)1.04	6)14.16	7)57.4	4)173.6	8)5.76
2.	5)17.25	6)18.72	2).496	3)8.28	7)60.48	4)5.16
3.	6)1.092	2).6738	3)23.4	7)65.52	2)7.86	8)2.584

68A. Practice Set

▶ Divide. Check your answers.

	a	b	c	d	e	f
1.	3)1.89	4)25.2	8)69.76	4)30.24	9)97.2	8)4.864
2.	5)4.25	2)2.64	6)5.16	9)18.72	7)48.3	9)76.5
3.	9)8.172	3)1.89	4).48	7)3.017	2).6312	6)53.76
4.	5)17.25	8)697.6	7)65.52	4)2.408	8).9792	3)129.6

69. Inventory Test
More Challenging Exercises

▶ Divide. Check your answers.

	a	b	c	d	e
1.	37)66.6	18)43.74	21)90.3	48)432.0	9)3.114
2.	60)14.40	42)23.52	33)7.26	14)172.2	91)263.9
3.	25)207.5	86)9.46	75)11.700	57)96.9	63)176.4

69A. Practice Set

▶ Divide. Check your answers.

	a	b	c	d	e
1.	12)3.36	38)9.50	43)25.37	30)741.0	71)440.2
2.	24)9.84	46)96.6	15)6.795	52)49.92	69)9.66
3.	81)59.13	32)188.8	55)412.5	26)19.24	96)336.0
4.	11)47.63	85)12.75	38)4.142	49)303.8	57)26.79
5.	69)28.29	35)136.5	66)28.38	76)136.8	28)187.6

DIVISION WITH DECIMALS

When a divisor is <u>not</u> a whole number, you can rename it as a whole number by using these rules.

a. When the divisor has **one** decimal place, multiply the divisor <u>and</u> the dividend by **10.**

Problem	Work	New Problem
$3.6\overline{)17.28}$	$3.6 \times 10\overline{)17.28 \times 10}$	$36\overline{)172.8}$

b. When the divisor has **two** decimal places, multiply the divisor <u>and</u> the dividend by **100.**

Problem	Work	New Problem
$.39\overline{)26.52}$	$.39 \times 100\overline{)26.52 \times 100}$	$39\overline{)2652.}$

c. When the divisor has **three** decimal places, multiply the divisor <u>and</u> the dividend by **1000.**

Problem	Work	New Problem
$.005\overline{)0.6752}$	$.005 \times 1000\overline{).6752 \times 1000}$	$5\overline{)675.2}$

70. Inventory Test

Division with Decimals

▶ Rename each divisor and dividend. Then divide.

	a	b	c	d	e
1.	$1.6\overline{)64.32}$	$.64\overline{)1.984}$	$5.8\overline{)3.48}$	$.18\overline{).1494}$	$.04\overline{).216}$
2.	$.5\overline{)8.65}$	$.22\overline{)5.06}$	$4.1\overline{)42.64}$	$.15\overline{).225}$	$3.4\overline{)15.64}$
3.	$3.9\overline{).663}$	$.83\overline{)42.33}$	$.07\overline{).854}$	$.095\overline{).3135}$	$7.8\overline{)4.290}$

70A. Practice Set

▶ Divide. Check your answers.

	a	b	c	d	e
1.	.04)‾.152‾	1.3)‾2.73‾	2.1)‾.651‾	.67)‾6.164‾	.035)‾1.715‾
2.	.08)‾1.384‾	.72)‾.0864‾	3.4)‾3.808‾	.89)‾2.403‾	.042)‾.16884‾
3.	6.6)‾19.14‾	.23)‾.7843‾	5.5)‾264.0‾	4.8)‾176.16‾	.52)‾.0832‾

DIVISION WITH DECIMALS—SHORT METHOD

Here is a short method for multiplying the divisor and the dividend by 10, by 100, by 1000, and so on.

Short Method   **Examples**

1. To multiply by **10**, move each decimal point **one** place to the right.

   1.4)‾37.8‾

2. To multiply by **100**, move each decimal point **two** places to the right.

   .85)‾.64 8‾

3. To multiply by **1000**, move each decimal point **three** places to the right.

   .049)‾.264 6‾

Example: .08235 ÷ .183 = ?

Solution:
```
           .45
   .183 )‾.082 35‾
          73 2
          ─────
          9 15
          9 15
          ─────
             0
```

Check:
```
        45
      ×.183
      ─────
       135
      3600
      4500
      ──────
     .08235
```

70B. Practice Set

▶ Divide. Check your answers.

	a	b	c	d	e
1.	.5)‾.2635‾	1.7)‾15.47‾	.04)‾1.08‾	.6)‾243.6‾	.11)‾.231‾
2.	.003)‾.4212‾	.33)‾.1452‾	4.9)‾30.87‾	.9)‾12.33‾	.3)‾13.8‾
3.	4.3)‾7.31‾	.008)‾.2448‾	.6)‾2.3412‾	3.4)‾70.04‾	.17)‾.731‾

DIVISION WITH DECIMALS—USES OF ZEROS

Uses of Zeros	Examples

1. Sometimes one or more zeros must be inserted in the quotient in order to place the decimal point correctly.

$$\overset{.0009}{8)\overline{.0072}}$$

Check: $.0009 \times 8 = .0072$

2. Sometimes one or more zeros must be annexed to the dividend in order to place the decimal point correctly.

$$.06)\overline{36} \longrightarrow \overset{6\ 00.}{.06\,)\overline{36.00}}$$

Check: $600 \times .06 = 36$

3. Sometimes one or more zeros must be annexed after the decimal point in the dividend in order to carry out the division.

$$.017)\overline{81.6} \longrightarrow \overset{4\ 800.}{.017\,)\overline{81.600}}$$

Check: $4800 \times .017 = 81.6$

71. Inventory Test

▶ Divide. Check your answers.

	a	b	c	d	e
1.	$.7)\overline{574}$	$4.7)\overline{2.914}$	$.12)\overline{276}$	$.8)\overline{.0576}$	$.007)\overline{604.8}$
2.	$.9)\overline{378}$	$.03)\overline{82.8}$	$59)\overline{2.1122}$	$24)\overline{9}$	$.09)\overline{97.2}$
3.	$.005)\overline{125}$	$3.8)\overline{1.710}$	$.06)\overline{.852}$	$.31)\overline{.00992}$	$.2)\overline{.0026}$

71A. Practice Set

▶ Divide. Check your answers.

	a	b	c	d	e
1.	$1.4)\overline{.0196}$	$2.4)\overline{77.4}$	$.29)\overline{153.7}$	$.4)\overline{6.988}$	$.008)\overline{25.6}$
2.	$.087)\overline{41.76}$	$76)\overline{.4408}$	$6.5)\overline{62.40}$	$2.7)\overline{35.1}$	$4.1)\overline{205}$
3.	$5.2)\overline{.1768}$	$.98)\overline{48.608}$	$3.7)\overline{.31154}$	$30)\overline{6}$	$9)\overline{.216}$

ROUNDING QUOTIENTS

To round decimals, look at the digit to the right of the place to which you are rounding. If the digit is **less** than **5**, round **down.** If the digit is **5** or **more,** round **up.**

Rules

1. To find a quotient to the nearest tenth, divide to hundredths. Then round.

2. To find a quotient to the nearest hundredth, divide to thousandths. Then round.

Examples

1. $13.7 \div .6 \longrightarrow$ $.6\overline{)13.700}$ quotient 22.83

   22.83 rounded to the nearest **tenth** is **22.8.**

2. $4.3 \div .09 \longrightarrow$ $.09\overline{)4.30\,000}$ quotient 47.777

   47.777 rounded to the nearest **hundredth** is **47.78.**

If you need help with rounding, see pages 123, 124, and 126.

72. Inventory Test

▶ Divide. Find the quotient to the nearest tenth.

a	b	c	d	e
1. $5\overline{)12.7}$	$8\overline{)27.36}$	$.7\overline{)2.53}$	$.08\overline{)23.81}$	$.38\overline{)1.625}$

▶ Find the quotient to the nearest hundredth.

2. $.8\overline{).705}$	$6\overline{)273.1}$	$.09\overline{)23.41}$	$1.6\overline{)2.655}$	$3.2\overline{)24.58}$

72A. Practice Set

▶ Divide. Find the quotient to the nearest tenth.

a	b	c	d	e
1. $4\overline{)86.3}$	$.92\overline{)2.65}$	$.07\overline{).2362}$	$.6\overline{)19}$	$3.7\overline{).0777}$

▶ Find the quotient to the nearest hundredth.

2. $.6\overline{)8.32}$	$.05\overline{).07231}$	$8\overline{)5}$	$.28\overline{)2.19}$	$6\overline{).045}$
3. $6\overline{).25}$	$.3\overline{)1.9634}$	$.41\overline{).7215}$	$5.6\overline{).427}$	$2.5\overline{)7.432}$

WRITING DECIMALS FOR FRACTIONS

To write a decimal for a fraction, divide the numerator of the fraction by the denominator. Divide to hundredths.

Examples: Write a decimal for each fraction.

$$\text{a. } \tfrac{5}{8} \qquad\qquad\qquad\qquad \text{b. } \tfrac{1}{3}$$

Solutions: a. $\tfrac{5}{8}$ means $5 \div 8$.   **b.** $\tfrac{1}{3}$ means $1 \div 3$.

$$
\begin{array}{r}
.62\frac{4}{8} = .62\frac{1}{2} \\
8\overline{)5.00} \\
4\,8 \\
\hline
20 \\
16 \\
\hline
4
\end{array}
\qquad\qquad
\begin{array}{r}
.33\frac{1}{3} \\
3\overline{)1.00} \\
9 \\
\hline
10 \\
9 \\
\hline
1
\end{array}
$$

$$\tfrac{5}{8} = .62\tfrac{1}{2} \longleftarrow \text{You could also write .625 for } .62\tfrac{1}{2}. \qquad \tfrac{1}{3} = .33\tfrac{1}{3}$$

73. Inventory Test

▶ Write a decimal for each fraction.

	a	b	c	d	e	f	g	h
1.	$\frac{3}{4}$	$\frac{2}{3}$	$\frac{1}{20}$	$\frac{7}{10}$	$\frac{1}{12}$	$\frac{4}{25}$	$\frac{1}{4}$	$\frac{7}{8}$
2.	$\frac{5}{16}$	$\frac{1}{6}$	$\frac{7}{25}$	$\frac{3}{50}$	$\frac{1}{8}$	$\frac{5}{9}$	$\frac{27}{100}$	$\frac{2}{7}$
3.	$\frac{9}{200}$	$\frac{2}{5}$	$\frac{37}{100}$	$\frac{3}{8}$	$\frac{5}{6}$	$\frac{5}{12}$	$\frac{18}{50}$	$\frac{9}{10}$

73A. Practice Set

▶ Write a decimal for each fraction.

	a	b	c	d	e	f	g	h
1.	$\frac{3}{20}$	$\frac{3}{10}$	$\frac{1}{16}$	$\frac{8}{10}$	$\frac{1}{5}$	$\frac{7}{40}$	$\frac{11}{20}$	$\frac{1}{10}$
2.	$\frac{3}{11}$	$\frac{11}{200}$	$\frac{12}{25}$	$\frac{5}{7}$	$\frac{9}{16}$	$\frac{17}{25}$	$\frac{11}{12}$	$\frac{3}{7}$
3.	$\frac{8}{25}$	$\frac{7}{100}$	$\frac{29}{1000}$	$\frac{19}{20}$	$\frac{2}{11}$	$\frac{7}{9}$	$\frac{12}{25}$	$\frac{3}{40}$

▶ Find the answers. Write fractions in lowest terms.

1. 29,603
    8,277
    43,945
    +15,670

2. 845
    × 72

3. 3.7)‾31.08‾

4. $7\frac{3}{5}$
    $+4\frac{2}{3}$

5. Write a decimal for $\frac{9}{16}$.

6. $1\frac{1}{8} \div 5\frac{5}{8} =$

7. $7\frac{2}{5} \times \frac{5}{9} =$

8. 2.75
    18.03
    7.68
    + 2.92

9. 2.73
    ×.006

10. .6)‾270‾

Stop! Try the Survey Test on page 85 again. See if you can make a perfect score.

Career Capsule

Loan officers in banks help customers arrange for loans to make large purchases such as a car. Persons who borrow money must pay **interest,** or a **finance charge,** on the amount borrowed.

▶ In Exercises **1–6,** find the number of months it will take to repay each loan.

Example:

Total Amount Owed (Loan & Finance Charge)	Monthly Payment
$4554.12	$379.51

Solution: Number of Months = Total Amount Owed ÷ Monthly Payment

Number of Months = $4554.12 ÷ $379.51

Number of Months = **12**

	Total Amount Owed	Monthly Payment	Number of Months
1.	$3360.00	$140.00	?
2.	$6336.00	$132.00	?
3.	$4462.08	$371.84	?
4.	$5442.48	$226.77	?
5.	$3798.48	$316.54	?
6.	$6351.84	$132.33	?

APPLICATIONS

Food

The **unit price** is the price per ounce, per quart, per gram, per liter, and so on.

▶ In Exercises **1–10,** find the unit price. Carry the division to three decimal places when necessary.

Example: 5 kilogram bag of potatoes for $1.96

Solution: Unit Price $= \dfrac{\text{Cost of Potatoes}}{\text{Number of Kilograms}}$

Unit Price $= \dfrac{1.96}{5}$

Unit Price $=$ **$.392,** or **39.2¢,**

1. 2–kilogram bag of sugar for $.97
2. 4 quarts of milk for $1.94
3. 2 liters of juice for $.83
4. 195–gram can of tuna for $.78
5. 5–ounce jar of olive oil for $.79
6. 8–ounce jar of coffee for $3.88
7. 2–pound jar of peanut butter for $1.49
8. 3–kilogram bag of apples for $2.31
9. 5 grapefruit for $.96
10. 6 oranges for $1.23

Consumer Credit

11. Mark Jackson borrowed $435.20 to buy a stereo. He will pay $54.40 each month. How many months will it take him to repay the loan?

12. Ruth Klein borrowed $3,546.00 to buy a car. She will pay $98.50 each month. How many months will it take her to repay the loan?

Measurement

The table at the right shows the annual rainfall in centimeters for five cities during a recent year.

▶ In Exercises **13–16,** find the average monthly rainfall for each city. Round each answer to the nearest tenth of a centimeter.

City	Rainfall in Centimeters
Chicago	86.3
Dallas	90.5
Miami	142.0
New York	104.9
San Francisco	25.5

Example: Dallas

Solution: Average Monthly Rainfall $= \dfrac{\text{Annual Rainfall}}{12}$

Average Monthly Rainfall $= \dfrac{90.5}{12} = 7.54$ ◀——— Two decimal places

Average Monthly Rainfall $=$ **7.5 centimeters** ◀——— Nearest tenth

13. Chicago   14. New York   15. Miami   16. San Francisco

REVIEW OF APPLICATIONS: Decimals

▶In Exercises **1–26,** choose the correct answer. Choose **a, b, c,** or **d.**

▶In Exercises **1–6,** find the balance carried forward (BAL CAR'D FOR'D).

1.

| No. _1_ Amt. $75.99 |
| October 5 ___19___ |
| To _Tyne's Market_ |
| For _Groceries_ |

DOLLARS	CENTS	
190	62	BAL. BRO'T. FOR'D.
		AMT. DEPOSITED
		TOTAL
75	99	AMT: THIS CHECK
		MISCELLANEOUS DEDUCTION
?	?	BAL. CAR'D. FOR'D.

a. $266.61
b. $114.63
c. $115.63
d. $266.51

2.

| No. _2_ Amt. $11.00 |
| October 18 ___19___ |
| To _Medford_ |
| _Bicycle Shop_ |
| For _Repairs_ |

DOLLARS	CENTS	
295	50	BAL. BRO'T. FOR'D.
76	80	AMT. DEPOSITED
372	30	TOTAL
11	00	AMT. THIS CHECK
		MISCELLANEOUS DEDUCTION
?	?	BAL. CAR'D. FOR'D.

a. $361.30
b. $218.70
c. $372.30
d. $288.70

3.

| No. _3_ Amt. $385.76 |
| November 1 ___19___ |
| To _Carver_ |
| _Management Agency_ |
| For _Rent_ |

DOLLARS	CENTS	
25	60	BAL. BRO'T. FOR'D.
600	00	AMT. DEPOSITED
625	60	TOTAL
385	76	AMT. THIS CHECK
		MISCELLANEOUS DEDUCTION
?	?	BAL. CAR'D. FOR'D.

a. $1010.36
b. $1011.36
c. $239.84
d. $240.84

4.

| No. _4_ Amt. $189.95 |
| November 4 ___19___ |
| To _Dillon Department_ |
| _Store_ |
| For _Clothing_ |

DOLLARS	CENTS	
82	60	BAL. BRO'T. FOR'D.
150	50	AMT. DEPOSITED
233	10	TOTAL
189	95	AMT. THIS CHECK
		MISCELLANEOUS DEDUCTION
?	?	BAL. CAR'D. FOR'D.

a. $43.15
b. $143.15
c. $423.05
d. $422.05

5.

| No. _5_ Amt. $35.24 |
| November 9 ___19___ |
| To _Yorkville Laundry_ |
| For _Laundry_ |

DOLLARS	CENTS	
189	46	BAL. BRO'T. FOR'D.
25	59	AMT. DEPOSITED
		TOTAL
35	24	AMT. THIS CHECK
		MISCELLANEOUS DEDUCTION
?	?	BAL. CAR'D. FOR'D.

a. $250.29
b. $215.05
c. $179.81
d. $154.22

6.

| No. _6_ Amt. $50.06 |
| November 16 ___19___ |
| To _National Travel_ |
| For _Bus Ticket_ |

DOLLARS	CENTS	
374	18	BAL. BRO'T. FOR'D.
28	88	AMT. DEPOSITED
		TOTAL
50	06	AMT. THIS CHECK
		MISCELLANEOUS DEDUCTION
?	?	BAL. CAR'D. FOR'D.

a. $353.00
b. $453.12
c. $403.06
d. $345.30

The table below shows the cost per meter of four kinds of cloth.

▶ Use this table for Exercises **7–10.**

Cloth	Cotton	Polyester	Denim	Velour
Cost	$3.00	$5.00	$3.50	$6.50

7. Find the cost of 2.25 meters of cotton.
    a. $6.75   **b.** $6.65   **c.** $.68   **d.** $7.75

8. How much does 3.75 meters of polyester cost?
    a. $18.75   **b.** $18.55   **c.** $1.88   **d.** $15.75

9. Find the cost of 1.5 meters of denim.
    a. $.53   **b.** $5.05   **c.** $2.05   **d.** $5.25

10. How much does 2.5 meters of velour cost?
    a. $15.05   **b.** $16.25   **c.** $4.55   **d.** $1.63

11. The Mondello family estimates that their color TV uses 620 kilowatt hours of electricity per year. They pay $.059 per kilowatt hour for electricity.
Find the yearly cost of running the color T.V.
    a. $36.58   **b.** $36.48   **c.** $365.80   **d.** $364.80

12. Mrs. Conklin estimates that the clothes dryer uses 1200 kilowatt hours of electricity per year. She pays $.055 per kilowatt hour for electricity.
How much is the yearly cost of operating the clothes dryer?
    a. $56.00   **b.** $560.00   **c.** $660.00   **d.** $66.00

13. Mr. Cox estimates that the water heater uses 4900 kilowatt hours of electricity in one year. The cost of electricity in his town is $.056 per kilowatt hour.
Find the yearly cost of operating the water heater.
    a. $27.44   **b.** $2,744   **c.** $274.40   **d.** $264.40

14. Paul Chen borrowed $937.50 for home improvements. He will pay $62.50 each month on the loan.
How many months will it take for him to repay the loan?
    a. 15   **b.** 1.25   **c.** 1.5   **d.** 12

15. Margarita Duran borrowed $2,859 to buy a new car. She will pay $95.30 per month on the loan.
How many months will it take to repay the loan?
    a. 2.5   **b.** 3   **c.** 36   **d.** 30

16. Oranges sell at 5 for $1.05.
Find the unit price.
    a. 21¢   **b.** $5.25   **c.** $1.10   **d.** 25¢

17. Rolls cost 8 for $.84.
Find the unit price.

    a. $10.50   **b.** $1.05   **c.** 10.5¢   **d.** 1.05¢

18. A 16-ounce jar of vinegar costs $.24.
Find the unit price.

    a. .15¢   **b.** $1.50   **c.** $.015   **d.** 15¢

19. A 15-ounce jar of applesauce sells for $.42.
Find the unit price.

    a. $.28   **b.** 28¢   **c.** .028¢   **d.** $.028

20. The price of 2.5 kilograms of ground beef is $9.90.
Find the unit price.

    a. $.396   **b.** $3.96   **c.** 39.6¢   **d.** 30.96¢

21. The price of a 312-gram box of cereal is $1.56.
What is the unit price?

    a. $.05   **b.** 5¢   **c.** $.50   **d.** $.005

22. About 31.3 centimeters of rain fell in Salt Lake City during a recent year.
Find the average monthly rainfall to the nearest tenth of a centimeter.

    a. 2.6   **b.** 2.4   **c.** 26.1   **d.** 2.7

23. Approximately 96.7 centimeters of rain fell in Washington, D.C. during a recent year.
Find the average monthly rainfall to the nearest tenth of a centimeter.

    a. 8.0   **b.** .8   **c.** 80.6   **d.** 8.1

24. A bedroom is 5 meters long, 5 meters wide, and 2.5 meters high.
Find the volume of the room in cubic meters.

    a. 62.5   **b.** 6.25

    c. 12.5   **d.** 25

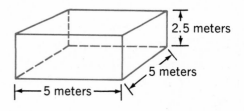

25. A living room is 8.5 meters long, 7 meters wide, and 2.5 meters high.
Find the volume of the room in cubic meters.

    a. 18   **b.** 14.875

    c. 59.5   **d.** 148.75

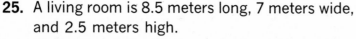

26. A playroom is 9 meters long, 7.5 meters wide, and 2.5 meters high.
Find the volume of the room in cubic meters.

    a. 16.875   **b.** 19

    c. 168.75   **d.** 67.5

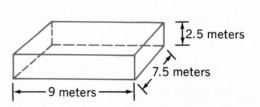

REVIEW OF SKILLS: Whole Numbers, Fractions, and Decimals

▶ Complete this puzzle. Write the answers to the exercises in the boxes of the puzzle. The answers should check across and down. Each box holds one digit.

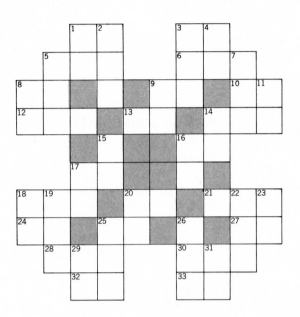

ACROSS	DOWN
1. $17 \times 5 = \underline{\quad}$	**1.** $32 \times 2.5 = \underline{\quad}$
3. L.C.D. for $\frac{2}{3}$, $\frac{5}{6}$, and $\frac{4}{7}$ is $\underline{\quad}$	**2.** $157 + 139 + 204 = \underline{\quad}$
5. $850 \div 8.5 = \underline{\quad}$	**3.** $2\frac{2}{5} \times 180 = \underline{\quad}$
6. $1246 - 894 = \underline{\quad}$	**4.** $.25\overline{)6.25} = \underline{\quad}$
8. $.08\overline{)3.2} = \underline{\quad}$	**5.** $1785 \div 17 = \underline{\quad}$
9. $52.5 \times .8 = \underline{\quad}$	**7.** $12 \div \frac{1}{20} = \underline{\quad}$
10. $17.72 + 21.9 + 6.38 = \underline{\quad}$	**8.** $192 \times .25 = \underline{\quad}$
12. $3743 - 2891 = \underline{\quad}$	**9.** $50 \times \frac{9}{10} = \underline{\quad}$
13. $1.5 \times 50 = \underline{\quad}$	**11.** $24 \times 2\frac{1}{2} = \underline{\quad}$
14. $20 \div .2 = \underline{\quad}$	**14.** $.182\overline{)1.82} = \underline{\quad}$
16. $180 \times \frac{1}{3} = \underline{\quad}$	**15.** $5\frac{1}{8} \div \frac{1}{16} = \underline{\quad}$
17. $2\frac{3}{4} + 5\frac{7}{12} + 3\frac{2}{3} = \underline{\quad}$	**16.** $4 \times 4 \times 4 = \underline{\quad}$
18. $17,500 \div 100 = \underline{\quad}$	**17.** $6.04 + 8.96 = \underline{\quad}$
20. $3 \times 2 \times 2 \times 2 = \underline{\quad}$	**18.** $90 \times .2 = \underline{\quad}$
21. $17 \times 13 = \underline{\quad}$	**19.** $934 - 165 = \underline{\quad}$
24. $172\overline{)14,792} = \underline{\quad}$	**20.** $1\frac{1}{2} \div \frac{3}{40} = \underline{\quad}$
25. $2\frac{2}{3} \times 22\frac{1}{2} = \underline{\quad}$	**22.** $58 \times 5 = \underline{\quad}$
27. $19 \times 5 = \underline{\quad}$	**23.** $7.46 + 9.75 - 2.21 = \underline{\quad}$
28. $.012\overline{)11.4} = \underline{\quad}$	**25.** $25 \times 24 = \underline{\quad}$
30. $500 \times .9 = \underline{\quad}$	**26.** $81,000 \times .008 = \underline{\quad}$
32. $3\frac{1}{8} + 8\frac{5}{6} - 1\frac{23}{24} = \underline{\quad}$	**29.** $.03 \times 1700 = \underline{\quad}$
33. $13,054 - 12,969 = \underline{\quad}$	**31.** $66 \div 1\frac{1}{5} = \underline{\quad}$

79. Inventory Test

Writing Decimals for Per Cents

▶ Write a decimal and a fraction in lowest terms for each per cent.

	a	b	c	d	e	f
1.	80%	44%	$33\frac{1}{3}$%	$66\frac{2}{3}$%	$12\frac{1}{2}$%	67%
2.	75%	27%	85%	$1\frac{1}{2}$%	45%	24%
3.	52%	63%	5%	$7\frac{1}{2}$%	$16\frac{2}{3}$%	$17\frac{1}{2}$%

79A. Practice Set

▶ Write a decimal and a fraction in lowest terms for each per cent.

	a	b	c	d	e	f
1.	70%	4%	$83\frac{1}{3}$%	$3\frac{1}{2}$%	76%	$8\frac{1}{3}$%
2.	50%	49%	20%	1%	35%	25%
3.	36%	$11\frac{1}{9}$%	$9\frac{1}{2}$%	$\frac{1}{2}$%	8%	97%
4.	$37\frac{1}{2}$%	$87\frac{1}{2}$%	12%	55%	$13\frac{1}{2}$%	19%
5.	46%	60%	10%	15%	$4\frac{1}{4}$%	54%

FINDING A PER CENT OF A NUMBER USING DECIMALS

To find a per cent of a number, write a decimal for the per cent. Then multiply.

Examples: **a.** Find 72% of 350.   **b.** Find 9% of 620.

Solutions: **a.** 72% = .72

$$
\begin{array}{r}
350 \\
\times\ .72 \\
\hline
7\ 00 \\
245\ 00 \\
\hline
252.00
\end{array}
$$

72% of 350 = **252**

b. 9% = .09

$$
\begin{array}{r}
620 \\
\times\ .09 \\
\hline
55.80
\end{array}
$$

9% of 620 = **55.8**

---

80. Inventory Test

Finding a Per Cent of a Number Using Decimals

▶ Find each of the following.

a	b	c
1. 25% of 48 =	8% of 300 =	75% of 600 =
2. 60% of 45 =	27% of 200 =	9% of 200 =
3. 18% of 75 =	4% of 625 =	38% of 700 =
4. 72% of 65 =	98% of 45 =	2% of 720 =
5. 5% of 180 =	90% of 700 =	85% of 600 =
6. 46% of 90 =	32% of 750 =	12% of 500 =

80A. Practice Set

▶ Find each of the following.

a	b	c
1. 36% of 450 =	88% of 750 =	95% of 780 =
2. 22% of 95 =	6% of 520 =	16% of 525 =
3. 18% of 600 =	27% of 90 =	40% of 800 =
4. 73% of 480 =	50% of 768 =	91% of 300 =
5. 60% of 350 =	1% of 76 =	7% of 480 =

IMPORTANT EQUIVALENTS

Some per cents and their fraction equivalents are used so often that you should memorize them. This table will help you.

$1\% = .01 = \frac{1}{100}$	$70\% = .70 = \frac{7}{10}$	$12\frac{1}{2}\% = .12\frac{1}{2}$ or $.125 = \frac{1}{8}$
$10\% = .10 = \frac{1}{10}$	$80\% = .80 = \frac{4}{5}$	$37\frac{1}{2}\% = .37\frac{1}{2}$ or $.375 = \frac{3}{8}$
$20\% = .20 = \frac{1}{5}$	$90\% = .90 = \frac{9}{10}$	$62\frac{1}{2}\% = .62\frac{1}{2}$ or $.625 = \frac{5}{8}$
$30\% = .30 = \frac{3}{10}$	$25\% = .25 = \frac{1}{4}$	$87\frac{1}{2}\% = .87\frac{1}{2}$ or $.875 = \frac{7}{8}$
$40\% = .40 = \frac{2}{5}$	$75\% = .75 = \frac{3}{4}$	$16\frac{2}{3}\% = .16\frac{2}{3} = \frac{1}{6}$
$50\% = .50 = \frac{1}{2}$	$33\frac{1}{3}\% = .33\frac{1}{3} = \frac{1}{3}$	$83\frac{1}{3}\% = .83\frac{1}{3} = \frac{5}{6}$
$60\% = .60 = \frac{3}{5}$	$66\frac{2}{3}\% = .66\frac{2}{3} = \frac{2}{3}$	$100\% = 1.00 = 1$

FINDING A PER CENT OF A NUMBER USING FRACTIONS

To find a per cent of a number, write a fraction for the per cent. Then multiply.

Sometimes you can use the list of Important Equivalents on page 105 to help you write a fraction for a per cent.

Examples: a. Find 15% of 600.   **b.** Find $37\frac{1}{2}$% of 480.

Solutions: a. $15\% = \frac{15}{100} = \frac{3}{20}$ **b.** $37\frac{1}{2}\% = \frac{3}{8}$ ⟵ From the list on page 105.

$$\frac{3}{20} \times 600 = \frac{3}{\underset{1}{20}} \times \frac{\overset{30}{600}}{1}$$ $$\frac{3}{8} \times 480 = \frac{3}{\underset{1}{8}} \times \frac{\overset{60}{480}}{1}$$

$$= \frac{3 \times 30}{1 \times 1} = \textbf{90}$$ $$= \frac{3 \times 60}{1 \times 1} = \textbf{180}$$

81. Inventory Test

Finding a Per Cent of a Number Using Equivalent Fractions

▶Find each answer. Write an equivalent fraction for each per cent.

	a	b	c
1.	25% of 72 =	30% of 85 =	80% of 40 =
2.	$33\frac{1}{3}$% of 96 =	$66\frac{2}{3}$% of 720 =	70% of 80 =
3.	75% of 240 =	40% of 860 =	$87\frac{1}{2}$% of 56 =
4.	$16\frac{2}{3}$% of 66 =	$83\frac{1}{3}$% of 144 =	20% of 80 =
5.	90% of 700 =	50% of 942 =	30% of 900 =

81A. Practice Set

▶Find each answer. Write an equivalent fraction for each per cent.

	a	b	c
1.	$66\frac{2}{3}$% of 630 =	$87\frac{1}{2}$% of 360 =	80% of 800 =
2.	90% of 800 =	70% of 900 =	$37\frac{1}{2}$% of 104 =
3.	25% of 104 =	$16\frac{2}{3}$% of 6000 =	50% of 756 =
4.	$83\frac{1}{3}$% of 84 =	20% of 750 =	$12\frac{1}{2}$% of 888 =
5.	25% of 48 =	$33\frac{1}{3}$% of 873 =	10% of 892 =
6.	$87\frac{1}{2}$% of 400 =	$62\frac{1}{2}$% of 120 =	75% of 700 =

FINDING A PER CENT OF A NUMBER

To find a per cent of a number:

1. Write a decimal or a fraction for the per cent.
2. Multiply the given number by the decimal or the fraction.

82. Inventory Test

Finding a Per Cent of a Number—Review

▶ Find each answer.

a	b	c
1. 30% of 65 =	85% of 200 =	27% of 55 =
2. $62\frac{1}{2}$% of 192 =	15% of 40 =	$16\frac{2}{3}$% of 90 =
3. 6% of 800 =	$62\frac{1}{2}$% of 24 =	25% of 648 =
4. 47% of 530 =	$33\frac{1}{3}$% of 612 =	1% of 250 =

82A. Practice Set

▶ Find each answer.

a	b	c
1. 75% of 340 =	$37\frac{1}{2}$% of 80 =	$12\frac{1}{2}$% of 800 =
2. $83\frac{1}{3}$% of 300 =	72% of 600 =	$33\frac{1}{3}$% of 252 =
3. $66\frac{2}{3}$% of 324 =	19% of 30 =	9% of 250 =
4. 25% of 964 =	$62\frac{1}{2}$% of 200 =	$16\frac{2}{3}$% of 264

Career Capsule

Some **salespersons** receive a per cent of the selling price for each item they sell. The amount they receive is called a **commission.**

FMC	1.40	5.6	6	75 25½	24¾
FMC pf	2.25	6.9	...	14 33	32½
Fabrge	.40	3.9	9	145 10½	10
FabriCtr	.28	5.5	5	5 5¼	5⅛
FacetEnt	.15e	2.7	80	34 5¾	5⅝
Fairchd s	1.20	2.8	6	335 42½	41⅞
FairmtF	.76	5.3	13	212 14⅜	13⅞
FamDir	.40	3.1	7	6 12¾	12½
FarahMf		......		49 4¼	4⅛
Fedders		......		95 3½	3⅜
FedCo	2.40	6.6	7	21 36⅝	36¼
FedExpr		...	11	629 46	43⅝
FdMog s	1.08	6.6	5	102 16½	16

▶ In Exercises **1–2,** find the commission.

Example: A 5% commission on sales of $5200.

Solution: 5% of $5200 = .05 × 5200
= **$260.00**

1. A real estate agent received a 6% commission on a house sold for $95,000.

2. A stockbroker received a 4% commission on a sale that amounted to $95.

107

APPLICATIONS

Clothing

You can save money by buying items on sale. The **discount** is the amount you save when the regular price is reduced.

> SALE!
> Boots
> 30% off
> Regular Price of
> $55

▶ In Exercises **1–4,** find the discount.

Example: Boots   **Solution: Discount = Regular Price × Rate of Discount**

Discount = $55   ×   30%

Discount = $55   ×   .30   = **$16.50**

1.
> SALE!
> Shoes
> 20% off
> Regular Price of
> $45

2.
> SALE!
> Sweaters
> 40% off
> Regular Price of
> $22

3.
> SALE!
> Wool Rugs
> 25% off
> Regular Price of
> $350

4.
> SALE!
> Coats
> 55% off
> Regular Price of
> $80

Taxation

The table at the right shows the rate of sales tax for five states in a recent year.

State	Rate
Colorado	3%
Florida	4%
Kentucky	5%
Connecticut	7%
Oklahoma	2%

▶ In Exercises **5–8,** find the sales tax in each state on a purchase of $80.

Example: Florida   **Solution:** $80 × 4% = $80 × .04

= **$3.20**

5. Oklahoma   **6.** Colorado   **7.** Connecticut   **8.** Kentucky

▶ In Exercises **9–12,** find the sales tax in each state on a purchase of $120.

9. Oklahoma   **10.** Florida   **11.** Colorado   **12.** Connecticut

Graphs

About 67,000,000 tons of paper were produced in the United States in a recent year. The circle graph at the right shows what per cent of the paper was used for different purposes.

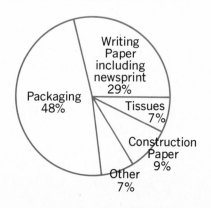

▶ In Exercises **13–16,** use the graph to find how many tons of paper were used for each purpose.

13. Tissues   **14.** Construction Paper

15. Writing Paper   **16.** Packaging

WRITING PER CENTS FOR FRACTIONS

To write a per cent for a fraction, divide the numerator of the fraction by the denominator. Carry the division out to two decimal places.

   Sometimes you can use the list of <u>Important Equivalents</u> on page 105.

Example: Write a per cent for $\frac{15}{24}$.

By Computation

Solutions: $\frac{15}{24} = \frac{5}{8}$ ⟵ Lowest terms

$$\frac{5}{8} \rightarrow 8\overline{)5.00} \quad .62\frac{4}{8}$$

$$\begin{array}{r} .62\frac{4}{8} \\ 8\overline{)5.00} \\ 4\,8 \\ \hline 20 \\ 16 \\ \hline 4 \end{array}$$

Don't forget the remainder

$$.62\tfrac{4}{8} = .62\tfrac{1}{2} = \frac{62\tfrac{1}{2}}{100} = \mathbf{62\tfrac{1}{2}\%}$$

Using the List of Important Equivalents

$\frac{15}{24} = \frac{5}{8}$ ⟵ Lowest terms

$= \mathbf{62\tfrac{1}{2}\%}$ ⟵ From the List

83. Inventory Test

▶ Write a per cent for each fraction.

	a	b	c	d	e	f
1.	$\frac{3}{5}$	$\frac{15}{20}$	$\frac{14}{16}$	$\frac{8}{16}$	$\frac{4}{16}$	$\frac{9}{12}$
2.	$\frac{7}{21}$	$\frac{5}{25}$	$\frac{6}{30}$	$\frac{2}{8}$	$\frac{3}{18}$	$\frac{9}{24}$

83A. Practice Set

▶ Write a per cent for each fraction.

	a	b	c	d	e	f
1.	$\frac{3}{4}$	$\frac{14}{20}$	$\frac{30}{36}$	$\frac{8}{32}$	$\frac{12}{32}$	$\frac{15}{50}$
2.	$\frac{21}{24}$	$\frac{15}{75}$	$\frac{8}{25}$	$\frac{12}{18}$	$\frac{8}{12}$	$\frac{4}{50}$
3.	$\frac{15}{24}$	$\frac{4}{24}$	$\frac{6}{16}$	$\frac{15}{48}$	$\frac{21}{49}$	$\frac{6}{50}$

FINDING WHAT PER CENT ONE NUMBER IS OF ANOTHER

To find what per cent one number is of another, write a fraction for the per cent. Then divide.

____% of 20 = 13   means $\frac{13}{20} = $ ____%.

____% of 63 = 18   means $\frac{18}{63} = $ ____%.

Examples: a. ____% of 20 = 13   b. ____% of 63 = 18

Solutions: a. $\frac{13}{20} = 13 \div 20$ b. $\frac{18}{63} = \frac{2}{7}$ ← Lowest terms

$= 2 \div 7$

$$\begin{array}{r} .65 \\ 20\overline{)13.00} \\ 12\ 0 \\ \hline 1\ 00 \\ 1\ 00 \\ \hline \end{array}$$ ← Two decimal places

$$\begin{array}{r} .28\frac{4}{7} \\ 7\overline{)2.00} \\ 1\ 4 \\ \hline 60 \\ 56 \\ \hline 4 \end{array}$$ Don't forget the remainder.

.65 = **65%** ← 13 is 65% of 20.

$.28\frac{4}{7} = \mathbf{28\frac{4}{7}\%}$ ← 18 is $28\frac{4}{7}$% of 63.

84. Inventory Test

▶ Find each answer.

a	b	c
1. ___% of 24 = 12	___% of 16 = 10	___% of 12 = 9
2. ___% of 16 = 4	___% of 60 = 30	___% of 25 = 10
3. ___% of 30 = 6	___% of 40 = 12	___% of 36 = 12
4. ___% of 50 = 15	___% of 32 = 20	___% of 72 = 18

84A. Practice Set

▶ Find each answer.

a	b	c
1. ___% of 40 = 8	___% of 64 = 16	___% of 12 = 3
2. ___% of 72 = 27	___% of 96 = 24	___% of 42 = 35
3. ___% of 62 = 31	___% of 48 = 18	___% of 75 = 25
4. ___% of 18 = 3	___% of 85 = 17	___% of 720 = 72
5. ___% of 64 = 48	___% of 70 = 21	___% of 25 = 16

PER CENT PROBLEMS—REVIEW

You have studied two types of per cent problems. Recognizing the type of per cent problem will help you to solve it.

Examples: Type 1   **Solutions**

	Step 1	Step 2
9% of 86 = ___	9% = .09	$.09 \times 86 = $ **7.74**
$62\frac{1}{2}$% of 144 = ___	$62\frac{1}{2}$% = $\frac{5}{8}$	$\frac{5}{8} \times \frac{\overset{18}{\cancel{144}}}{1} = $ **90**

Examples: Type 2   **Solutions**

___% of 63 = 18	$\frac{18}{63} = \frac{2}{7}$	$\frac{2}{7} \longrightarrow 7\overline{)2.00} = .28\frac{4}{7} = $ **$28\frac{4}{7}$%**
___% of 27 = 18	$\frac{18}{27} = \frac{2}{3}$	$\frac{2}{3} \longrightarrow 3\overline{)2.00} = .66\frac{2}{3} = $ **$66\frac{2}{3}$%**

85. Inventory Test

▶ Find each answer.

	a	b	c
1.	25% of 64 = ___	$66\frac{2}{3}$% of 240 = ___	$12\frac{1}{2}$% of 124 = ___
2.	32% of 60 = ___	___% of 66 = 22	___% of 72 = 54
3.	___% of 24 = 8	___% of 25 = 18	___% of 48 = 30
4.	___% of 50 = 11	42% of 500 = ___	8% of 600 = ___

85A. Practice Set

▶ Find each answer.

	a	b	c
1.	___% of 54 = 9	___% of 240 = 24	68% of 200 = ___
2.	36% of 55 = ___	45% of 90 = ___	___% of 76 = 19
3.	___% of 60 = 9	$33\frac{1}{3}$% of 720 = ___	___% of 32 = 28
4.	___% of 300 = 18	$83\frac{1}{3}$% of 540 = ___	___% of 25 = 7
5.	25% of 720 = ___	___% of 90 = 72	___% of 80 = 16

111

▶ Find the answers. Write fractions in lowest terms.

1. 80,273
   9,168
   43,074
   21,168
   + 5,392

2. 72.5
   × .43

3. $2\frac{3}{4} + 3\frac{5}{8} + 5\frac{2}{3} =$

4. .08)$\overline{24.8}$

5. $96 \times 12\frac{3}{4} =$

6. Write in lowest terms. $\frac{35}{63} =$

7. 80% of 750 =

8. ___% of 48 = 18

9. Write a fraction in lowest terms for this ratio: 19 to 38.

10. Juan bought a used car for $900. He paid 30% in cash. If the balance is to be paid in 15 equal monthly installments, how much must he pay each month?

Stop!   Try the Survey Test on page 102 again. See if you can make a perfect score.

APPLICATIONS

Probability

The chances or likelihood that an event will happen is called the **probability** of the event. To find probability, use this ratio.

$$\frac{\text{Number of Successful Ways}}{\text{Number of Possible Ways}} = \text{Probability Ratio}$$

A game uses a spinner like the one at the right.

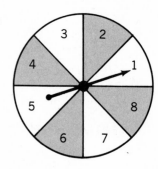

▶ In Exercises **1–6,** find the probability of each event. Write a fraction and a per cent for each probability.

Examples: **Event**   **Probability**

a. Stopping on a white region

a. $\frac{\text{Number of successful ways}}{\text{Number of possible ways}} = \frac{4}{8} = \frac{1}{2} = $ **50%**

b. Stopping on a 5

b. $\frac{\text{Number of successful ways}}{\text{Number of possible ways}} = \frac{1}{8} = $ **$12\frac{1}{2}$%**

c. Stopping on a 9
   (impossible event)

c. $\frac{\text{Number of successful ways}}{\text{Number of possible ways}} = \frac{0}{8} = 0 = $ **0%**

d. Stopping on a white or a red region
   (a certain event)

d. $\frac{\text{Number of successful ways}}{\text{Number of possible ways}} = \frac{8}{8} = 1 = $ **100%**

1. Stopping on a 4

2. Stopping on a red region

3. Stopping on a 10

4. Stopping on a number from 1 to 8

5. Stopping on a 2 or a 5

6. Stopping on a 1, 6, or 8

7. A weather forecaster says that there is a 90% chance of rain. What is the probability that it will <u>not</u> rain?

Per Cent—Part II

86. Survey Test

1. Write a per cent for each of the following.

   a $1\frac{3}{4}$ b 2.63 c $\frac{9}{2}$ d $2\frac{3}{8}$ e 4

2. Write a decimal and a fraction or mixed numeral for each per cent.

   a 150% b 200% c 220% d $412\frac{1}{2}\%$ e 128%

3. Find each of the following.

   a 120% of 85 = ___

   b ___% of 60 = 18

   c $12\frac{1}{2}\%$ of ___ = 5

   d ___% of 20 = 30

FINDING A NUMBER WHEN A PER CENT OF IT IS KNOWN

To find a number when a per cent of it is known:

1. Write a decimal or a fraction for the per cent.
2. Divide the number by the decimal or fraction.

Examples: **a.** 6% of ___ = 15

b. $87\frac{1}{2}\%$ of ___ = 21

Solutions: a.

b.

Step 1: Write a decimal for 6%.

$$6\% = .06$$

Step 1: Write a fraction for $87\frac{1}{2}\%$.

$$87\frac{1}{2}\% = \frac{7}{8} \longleftarrow \text{From the list on page 105.}$$

Step 2: Divide 15 by .06.

$$.06\overline{)1500}$$
$$250.$$

6% of **250** = 15

Step 2: Divide 21 by $\frac{7}{8}$.

$$21 \div \frac{7}{8} = \frac{21}{1} \times \frac{8}{7} = \frac{\overset{3}{21}}{1} \times \frac{8}{7}$$
$$= 24$$

$87\frac{1}{2}\%$ of **24** = 21

---

87. Inventory Test

▶ Find each of the following.

	a	b	c
1.	$\frac{3}{4}$ of ___ = 18	$\frac{2}{3}$ of ___ = 24	$\frac{2}{25}$ of ___ = 4
2.	50% of ___ = 48	25% of ___ = 18	$12\frac{1}{2}\%$ of ___ = 8
3.	$33\frac{1}{3}\%$ of ___ = 24	40% of ___ = 12	30% of ___ = 18
4.	60% of ___ = 12	92% of ___ = 23	$87\frac{1}{2}\%$ of ___ = 49

87A. Practice Set

▶ Find each of the following.

a	b	c
1. 10% of ___ = 40	$16\frac{2}{3}$% of ___ = 7	80% of ___ = 72
2. 6% of ___ = 15	35% of ___ = 7	75% of ___ = 144
3. 40% of ___ = 20	3% of ___ = 36	$37\frac{1}{2}$% of ___ = 60
4. 25% of ___ = 13	$12\frac{1}{2}$% of ___ = 9	1% of ___ = 2

PER CENTS GREATER THAN 100%

To write a per cent for $1\frac{1}{2}$, think:

$1 = 100\%$ $\frac{1}{2} = 50\%$

So, $1\frac{1}{2} = 100\% + 50\% = 150\%$.

1	+	$\frac{1}{2}$	=	$1\frac{1}{2}$
100%	+	50%	=	150%

Examples: Write a per cent for each of the following.

      a. $\frac{9}{2}$ **b.** 3.25

Solutions: a. $\frac{9}{2} = 4\frac{1}{2}$ **b.** 3.25 = 3 + .25

          $4 = 400\%$ $\frac{1}{2} = 50\%$ $3 = 300\%$ .25 = 25%

          So $\frac{9}{2} = 400\% + 50\% = $ **450%**   So 3.25 = 300% + 25% = **325%**

You can write a decimal for a per cent. Then you can write a whole number or a mixed numeral for the decimal.

   $400\% = 4.00 = $ **4** $112\frac{1}{2}\% = 1.12\frac{1}{2} = 1\frac{1}{8}$ ◀──── $.12\frac{1}{2} = \frac{1}{8}$

---

88. Inventory Test

▶ Write a per cent for each of the following.

	a	b	c	d	e	f	g
1.	$1\frac{1}{4}$	2.25	$\frac{8}{5}$	$4\frac{1}{2}$	$\frac{9}{4}$	1.27	3
2.	$2\frac{1}{2}$	$\frac{4}{3}$	$1\frac{3}{4}$	6.75	$3\frac{1}{8}$	3.05	$\frac{7}{2}$

▶ Write a decimal for each per cent. Then write a whole number or a mixed numeral for each decimal.

	a	b	c	d	e	f	g
3.	125%	100%	250%	820%	200%	525%	245%
4.	215%	375%	$412\frac{1}{2}\%$	170%	$187\frac{1}{2}\%$	120%	800%

▶ Write a per cent for each of the following.

	a	b	c	d	e	f	g
1.	$1\frac{1}{2}$	3.25	$\frac{5}{3}$	5.5	4	3.72	$\frac{7}{5}$
2.	$\frac{5}{2}$	$1\frac{7}{8}$	2.80	$4\frac{1}{8}$	$1\frac{1}{6}$	10	$1.33\frac{1}{3}$

▶ Write a decimal and a mixed numeral for each per cent.

	a	b	c	d	e	f	g
3.	350%	200%	345%	$137\frac{1}{2}$%	260%	160%	705%
4.	175%	140%	600%	425%	115%	390%	$266\frac{2}{3}$%

PER CENT PROBLEMS—REVIEW

Recognizing the type of per cent problem you are asked to solve will help you to solve the problem.

Examples: Type 1 **Solutions**

	Step 1	**Step 2**
50% of 76 = ___	50% = .50	$.50 \times 76 =$ **38.00**, or **38**
$12\frac{1}{2}$% of 56 = ___	$12\frac{1}{2}$% = $\frac{1}{8}$	$\frac{1}{\overset{1}{8}} \times \frac{\overset{7}{56}}{1} = \frac{7}{1} = 7$

Examples: Type 2 **Solutions**

___% of 45 = 9	$\frac{9}{45} = \frac{1}{5}$	$\frac{1}{5} \longrightarrow 5\overline{)1.00} = .20 =$ **20%**
___% of 90 = 30	$\frac{30}{90} = \frac{1}{3}$	$\frac{1}{3} \longrightarrow 3\overline{)1.00} = .33\frac{1}{3} =$ **$33\frac{1}{3}$%**

Examples: Type 3

7% of ___ = 35	7% = .07	$.07\overline{)3500.} =$ **500**
$83\frac{1}{3}$% of ___ = 55	$83\frac{1}{3}$% = $\frac{5}{6}$	$55 \div \frac{5}{6} = \frac{\overset{11}{55}}{1} \times \frac{6}{\underset{1}{5}} =$ **66**

89. Inventory Test

Miscellaneous Per Cent Problems

	a	b	c
1.	50% of ___ = 16	___% of 48 = 36	$12\frac{1}{2}$% of ___ = 32
2.	$37\frac{1}{2}$% of 72 = ___	$66\frac{2}{3}$% of ___ = 24	60% of 45 = ___
3.	125% of 80 = ___	2% of 505 = ___	___% of 50 = 1
4.	___% of 25 = 16	___% of 90 = 120	$66\frac{2}{3}$% of 60 = ___

89A. Practice Set

▶ Find each answer.

a	b	c
1. 250% of 32 = ___	___% of 108 = 36	$87\frac{1}{2}$% of 200 = ___
2. 45% of ___ = 135	2% of ___ = 4	___% of 40 = 2
3. ___% of 96 = 72	275% of 60 = ___	300% of 72 = ___
4. $33\frac{1}{3}$% of ___ = 15	$16\frac{2}{3}$% of 144 = ___	___% of 288 = 72
5. 24% of 75 = ___	90% of 80 = ___	25% of ___ = 16

89B. Practice Set

▶ Find each answer.

a	b	c
1. 15% of ___ = 60	92% of 500 = ___	$16\frac{2}{3}$% of 126 = ___
2. ___% of 70 = 56	75% of ___ = 108	___% of 40 = 3
3. $12\frac{1}{2}$% of 400 = ___	300% of ___ = 240	$33\frac{1}{3}$% of 600 = ___
4. 40% of ___ = 48	$62\frac{1}{2}$% of 168 = ___	$187\frac{1}{2}$% of 16 = ___
5. 4 = $16\frac{2}{3}$% of ___	12 = ___% of 16	___% of 18 = 8

Keeping Pace

▶ Find the answers. Write fractions in lowest terms.

1.
$$\begin{array}{r} 2.752 \\ .803 \\ +3.116 \\ \hline \end{array}$$

2.
$$\begin{array}{r} 2.000 \\ -1.735 \\ \hline \end{array}$$

3. $6\frac{1}{2} \times \frac{4}{5} \times 1\frac{7}{8} =$

4. $5\frac{3}{8} \div 2\frac{1}{2} =$

5. $.12\overline{).516}$

6. $37\frac{1}{2}$% of 136 = ___

7. 175% of 120 = ___

8. ___% of 90 = 63

9. 50 = ___% of 250

10. 8% of ___ = 12

Stop! Try the Survey Test on page 113 again. See if you can make a perfect score.

APPLICATIONS

Transportation

▶ In Exercises **1–4,** find the regular price of each trip.

Example: Each student obtains a 75% discount of $2.25 for a trip from Tarrytown to New York City.

Solution: 75% of ___ = $2.25

75% = .75

$$.75\overline{)2.25}\quad 3.$$

The regular price is **$3.00.**

1. Mrs. Milton is a senior citizen. She obtains a 50% discount of $2.00 for a trip from Garrison to New York City.

2. Dick Devlin travels during off peak hours. He receives a 25% discount of $.50 for a trip from Riverdale to New York City.

3. Mr. Perez receives a 15% discount of $24 by flying from New York to Chicago on Thursday rather than on Friday.

4. Melissa takes advantage of the "Low Economy Fare" to fly round trip from San Francisco to Sydney, Australia. She receives a 33% discount of $265.32.

Food

The **recommended daily allowance,** or **RDA,** is the amount of protein, fat, carbohydrate, vitamins, and minerals that a person should include in each day's diet. The table at the right shows the amounts of protein, one vitamin (niacin), and three minerals in one serving of a certain cereal.

	Amount	Per Cent of RDA
Calcium	280 milligrams	20%
Iron	3 milligrams	$16\frac{2}{3}$%
Niacin	5 milligrams	25%
Phosphorus	252 milligrams	18%
Protein	12 grams	20%

▶ Use this table in Exercises **5–8,** to find the total RDA for each.

Example:

	Amount	Per Cent of RDA
Protein	12 grams	20%

Solution: 20% of ___ = 12 grams

$$20\% = \frac{1}{5}$$

$$12 \div \frac{1}{5} = \frac{12}{1} \times \frac{5}{1} = \textbf{60 grams}$$

5. Calcium   6. Niacin   7. Phosphorus   8. Iron

Measurement

9. The tank of Tim's car contains 15 gallons of gasoline. This is 60% of what the tank holds when full.
   How much does the full tank hold?

10. A truck is carrying 2100 gallons of gasoline. This is 75% of what the truck holds when full.
    How much does it hold when full?

REVIEW OF APPLICATIONS: Ratio, Proportion, and Per Cent

The table at the right shows the number of retail stores in a certain town.

Kind of Store	Number
Food	18
Clothing	4
Hardware	8
Pharmacy	6

▶ Use this table for Exercises **1–4.**

1. Write a fraction in lowest terms to show the ratio of the number of clothing stores to the number of food stores.

   a. $\frac{18}{4}$ b. $\frac{4}{18}$

   c. $\frac{9}{2}$ d. $\frac{2}{9}$

2. Write a fraction in lowest terms to show the ratio of the number of hardware stores to the number of food stores.

   a. $\frac{18}{8}$ b. $\frac{4}{9}$ c. $\frac{8}{18}$ d. $\frac{9}{4}$

3. Write a fraction in lowest terms to show the ratio of the number of hardware stores to the number of pharmacies.

   a. $\frac{8}{6}$ b. $\frac{3}{4}$ c. $\frac{4}{3}$ d. $\frac{6}{8}$

4. Write a fraction in lowest terms to show the ratio of the number of pharmacies to the number of food stores.

   a. $\frac{3}{1}$ b. $\frac{18}{6}$ c. $\frac{1}{3}$ d. $\frac{6}{18}$

▶ Use this scale for Exercises **5–7:**

$$1 \text{ centimeter} = 200 \text{ kilometers}$$

5. The map distance from Peoria to Pittsburgh is 4 centimeters. Find the real distance in kilometers.

   a. 800   b. 80   c. 8000   d. 8

6. The map distance between Miami and Raleigh is 5 centimeters. What is the real distance in kilometers between these two cities?

   a. 1000   b. 10,000   c. 100   d. 10

7. The map distance between Las Vegas and Bismarck is 8 centimeters. Find the real distance in kilometers.

   a. 16,000   b. 16   c. 1600   d. 160

8. Warm-up suits are regularly priced at $38. Marge bought a suit at a 20% discount sale. How much did she save?

   a. $6.60   b. $7.60   c. $.76   d. $30.40

9. Gil bought a jacket on sale for 25% off the regular price of $49. How much did he save?

   a. $11.85   b. $1.25   c. $12.25   d. $36.75

10. The rate of sales tax in Pennsylvania in a recent year was 6%. Find the sales tax on a purchase of $50 in Pennsylvania that year.

a. $30.00   **b.** $.30   **c.** $3.00   **d.** $53.00

11. The rate of sales tax in Idaho in a recent year was 3%. Find the sales tax on a purchase of $95 in Idaho that year.

a. $23.50   **b.** $2.85   **c.** $28.50   **d.** $97.85

12. Maine had a 5% sales tax in a recent year. Find the sales tax on a purchase of $140 in Maine in that year.

a. $.70   **b.** $70.00   **c.** $140.70   **d.** $7.00

A certain city has a population of 130,000. The circle graph at the right shows the per cent of the population in four age groups.

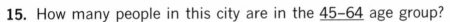

▶ Use this graph for Exercises **13–16.**

13. Find the number of people in this city in the 19 and under age group.

a. 44,200   **b.** 43,200
c. 4420   **d.** 432,000

14. How many people in the city are in the 20–44 age group?

a. 44,500   **b.** 4550
c. 45,500   **d.** 4450

15. How many people in this city are in the 45–64 age group?

a. 260   **b.** 260,000   **c.** 2600   **d.** 26,000

16. Find the number of people in this city in the 65 and over age group.

a. 1430   **b.** 14,300   **c.** 143,000   **d.** 143

A game uses a spinner like the one at the right.

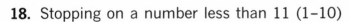

▶ In Exercises **17–22,** find the probability of each event.

17. Stopping on a 2

a. $\frac{2}{10}$ **b.** $\frac{1}{10}$
c. $\frac{2}{8}$, or $\frac{1}{4}$ **d.** $\frac{1}{8}$

18. Stopping on a number less than 11 (1–10)

a. $\frac{1}{10}$ **b.** $\frac{10}{10}$, or 1   **c.** $\frac{0}{10}$, or 0   **d.** $\frac{1}{8}$

19. Stopping on a 3 or a 7

a. $\frac{3}{7}$ **b.** $\frac{2}{8}$, or $\frac{1}{4}$ **c.** $\frac{2}{10}$, or $\frac{1}{5}$ **d.** $\frac{7}{10}$

20. Stopping on a red region
   a. 40%   **b.** 10%   **c.** 50%   **d.** 100%

21. Stopping on an odd number (1, 3, 5, 7, or 9)
   a. 50%   **b.** 10%   **c.** 100%   **d.** $62\frac{1}{2}$%

22. Stopping on a 12
   a. 100%   **b.** $\frac{0}{10}$, or 0%   **c.** $\frac{1}{12}$, or $8\frac{1}{3}$%   **d.** $\frac{1}{8}$, or $12\frac{1}{2}$%

23. A weather forecaster says that there is a 30% chance of snow. What are the chances that it will <u>not</u> snow?
   a. 30%   **b.** 50%   **c.** 0%   **d.** 70%

24. Mr. Hayer traveled by night coach to Miami. He received a 30% discount of $60 on this flight.
   Find the regular price for the trip.
   a. $20   **b.** $200   **c.** $18   **d.** $180

25. Dora traveled from Garrison to New York City during off peak hours. She received a 25% discount of $1.00.
   Find the regular price for the trip.
   a. $40   **b.** $2.50   **c.** $4.00   **d.** $.25

26. One serving of cheese contains 6 grams or 10% of the recommended daily allowance (RDA) for protein.
   Find the RDA in grams for protein.
   a. 60   **b.** 6

   c. .6   **d.** 600

27. A glass of milk contains 420 milligrams or 30% of the recommended daily allowance (RDA) for calcium.
   Find the RDA in milligrams for calcium.
   a. 140   **b.** 1400   **c.** 126   **d.** 1260

28. One serving of a certain cereal contains 6 milligrams or $33\frac{1}{3}$% of the recommended daily allowance (RDA) for iron.
   What is the RDA in milligrams for iron?
   a. 2   **b.** 180   **c.** 20   **d.** 18

29. The gas tank in Jan's car contains 8 gallons of gasoline. It is 40% full.
   Find the number of gallons the tank holds when full.
   a. 20   **b.** 3.2   **c.** 32   **d.** 2

30. The oil tank in the Martins' home contains 196 gallons of oil. This is 80% of what the tank holds when full.
   How many gallons does the tank hold when full?
   a. 1568   **b.** 156.8   **c.** 245   **d.** 24.5

REVIEW OF SKILLS: Whole Numbers, Fractions, Decimals, and Per Cent

▶ Complete this puzzle. Write the answers to the exercises in the boxes of the puzzle. The answers should check across and down. Each box holds one digit.

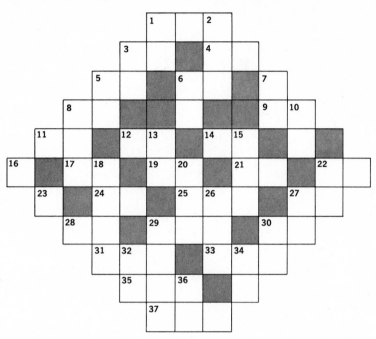

ACROSS

1. $5 \times 5 \times 5 \times 5 =$ ___

3. 80% of ___ = 56

4. $8 \div \frac{1}{5} =$ ___

5. $2\frac{1}{4} \times 6\frac{2}{3} =$ ___

6. ___% of 72 = 7.2

8. $192 \div 3 =$ ___

9. $2 \times 2 \times 3 \times 3 =$ ___

11. $2.4 \times 7.5 =$ ___

12. $24 =$ ___% of 32

14. $12 \times 4\frac{1}{4} =$ ___

17. $3\frac{2}{3} \div \frac{1}{6} =$ ___

19. 50% of 82 = ___

21. $.007\overline{)\,.588} =$ ___

22. ___% of 75 = 60

24. $1848 \div 88 =$ ___

25. $89 + 61 =$ ___

27. $3\frac{3}{8} + 6\frac{7}{24} + 4\frac{1}{3} =$ ___

28. $4\frac{1}{2} \times 3\frac{1}{3} =$ ___

29. 13% of 5000 = ___

30. $5.25 \times 8 =$ ___

31. $83\frac{1}{3}$% of 864 = ___

33. $25 \times 17 =$ ___

35. $2519 - 2231 =$ ___

37. $8.7\overline{)\,2175} =$ ___

DOWN

1. $3.75 \times 16 =$ ___

2. $4860 \div 9 =$ ___

3. $9.375 \times 8 =$ ___

5. $476\overline{)\,6664} =$ ___

6. $5.79 + 8.73 - 2.52 =$ ___

7. $13\frac{1}{2} \times 4\frac{2}{3} =$ ___

8. $40.92 \div .06 =$ ___

10. The reciprocal of $\frac{1}{64}$ is ___

13. $45 \times 1\frac{1}{5} =$ ___

15. $5 \times 3 \times 3 \times 4 =$ ___

16. $8\frac{1}{4} \div \frac{11}{12} =$ ___

18. $5321 - 3064 =$ ___

20. $2.9\overline{)\,333.5} =$ ___

22. $37\frac{1}{2}$% of 224 = ___

23. $1\frac{4}{5} \times 3\frac{1}{3} =$ ___

26. $28 \times 18 =$ ___

27. $8\frac{1}{2} + 6\frac{2}{5} - 2\frac{9}{10} =$ ___

29. $2024 + 1746 + 896 + 1416 =$ ___

30. 20% of ___ = 9

32. $8\frac{1}{4} \times \frac{5}{6} \times 3\frac{1}{5} =$ ___

34. $7.44 + 9.8 + 8.76 =$ ___

36. ___% of 20 = 17

Appendix

Whole Numbers

Rounding

> **Rules:** To round a whole number, look at the digit to the right of the place to which you are rounding.
> 1. If the digit is **less than 5**, round **down**.
> 2. If the digit is **5 or more**, round **up**.
>
> **Examples:**
> a. **6** rounded to the nearest ten is **10**.
> b. **55** rounded to the nearest ten is **60**.
> c. **650** rounded to the nearest hundred is **700**.
> d. **1742** rounded to the nearest hundred is **1700**.
> e. **8200** rounded to the nearest thousand is **8000**.
> f. **2865** rounded to the nearest thousand is **3000**.

▶Round to the nearest ten.

1. 13	**2.** 21	**3.** 155	**4.** 262	**5.** 1859	**6.** 6258

▶Round to the nearest hundred.

7. 542	**8.** 911	**9.** 109	**10.** 6258	**11.** 8770	**12** 4909

▶Round to the nearest thousand.

13. 1984	**14.** 1594	**15.** 1495	**16.** 12,706	**17.** 90,165	**18.** 64,500

Estimation

▶ Choose whichever gives the best estimate. Choose a, b, or c.

19. 25 + 32 + 86   a. 20 + 30 + 80   b. 30 + 40 + 90   c. 30 + 30 + 90

20. 410 + 757 + 320   a. 400 + 800 + 300   b. 400 + 700 + 300   c. 500 + 800 + 400

21. 710 − 585   a. 700 − 500   b. 700 − 600   c. 800 − 600

22. 3508 − 1798   a. 3000 − 2000   b. 4000 − 1000   c. 4000 − 2000

23. 42 × 38   a. 40 × 40   b. 40 × 30   c. 50 × 40

24. 385 × 207   a. 400 × 200   b. 300 × 200   c. 400 × 300

25. 89 ÷ 31   a. 80 ÷ 40   b. 90 ÷ 30   c. 90 ÷ 40

26. 1889 ÷ 98   a. 1000 ÷ 100   b. 1900 ÷ 100   c. 2000 ÷ 90

27. The base price of a new car is $5599. Power windows cost $210, an AM radio costs $78, and air conditioning costs $547. Estimate the total cost.
  a. $6800
  b. $5700
  c. $7000
  d. $8000

28. The base price of a new car is $3952. An AM/FM radio costs $178, power door locks cost $98, and door edge guards cost $12. Estimate the total cost.
  a. $4250
  b. $4500
  c. $4700
  d. $4900

29. The Hernanez family pays $378 per month for rent, $52 for utilities, and $28 for fire insurance. Estimate the total of these expenses.
  a. $430
  b. $460
  c. $490
  d. $500

30. The distance between Washington, D.C. and Seattle is 3221 kilometers. The distance between Washington, D.C. and Detroit is 554 kilometers. Estimate the difference in kilometers between the two distances.
  a. 2500
  b. 2000
  c. 3000
  d. 3500

31. The area of a basketball court is 1450 square meters. The area of a tennis court is 194 square meters. Estimate the difference in square meters between these areas.
  a. 900
  b. 1100
  c. 1300
  d. 1400

32. The area of a basketball court is 1450 square meters. The area of a baseball diamond is 752 square meters. Estimate the difference in square meters between these areas.
  a. 400
  b. 500
  c. 600
  d. 700

33. One glass of milk contains 159 calories. Estimate the number of calories in 19 glasses of milk.
  a. 1500
  b. 3200
  c. 2000
  d. 2500

34. Tomaso earns $1375.80 per month. Estimate how much he earns in 6 months.
  a. $6400
  b. $6000
  c. $5500
  d. $5000

35. The distance from Chicago to Cincinnati is 478 kilometers. Estimate the number of hours it would take a train travelling at 79 kilometers per hour to cover this distance.
  a. 5
  b. 6
  c. 7
  d. 8

Fractions

Rounding

> **Rules:**
> 1. If a fraction is **less than** $\frac{1}{2}$, round **down** to the nearest whole number.
> 2. If a fraction is **greater than** or **equal to** $\frac{1}{2}$, round **up** to the nearest whole number.
>
> **Examples:**
> a. $\frac{3}{4}$ rounded to the nearest whole number is **1**.
> b. $\frac{1}{6}$ rounded to the nearest whole number is **0**.
> c. $4\frac{2}{5}$ rounded to the nearest whole number is **4**.
> d. $5\frac{1}{2}$ rounded to the nearest whole number is **6**.
> e. $9\frac{7}{8}$ rounded to the nearest whole number is **10**.

▶ Round to the nearest whole number.

1. $\frac{7}{8}$ 2. $\frac{1}{5}$ 3. $\frac{4}{5}$ 4. $\frac{1}{9}$ 5. $\frac{15}{16}$ 6. $\frac{8}{9}$

7. $1\frac{6}{7}$ 8. $5\frac{3}{4}$ 9. $30\frac{1}{2}$ 10. $2\frac{1}{6}$ 11. $19\frac{2}{3}$ 12. $3\frac{4}{5}$

Estimation

▶ Choose whichever gives the best estimate. Choose a, b, or c.

		a.	b.	c.
13.	$2\frac{3}{4} + 5\frac{1}{9}$	$3 + 6$	$3 + 5$	$2 + 5$
14.	$58\frac{8}{9} - 9\frac{1}{5}$	$59 - 10$	$60 - 9$	$59 - 9$
15.	$16\frac{1}{3} \times \frac{19}{20}$	17×1	$17 \times \frac{1}{2}$	16×1
16.	$\frac{11}{12} \div \frac{15}{16}$	$\frac{1}{2} \div 1$	$1 \div 1$	$1 \div \frac{1}{2}$

▶ Choose whichever gives the best estimate. Choose a, b, c, or d.

17. It took Joanne $2\frac{3}{4}$ hours to travel from Miami to New York, $5\frac{1}{6}$ hours to travel from New York to Chicago, and $6\frac{3}{4}$ hours to travel from Chicago to Fairbanks.
Estimate her total travelling time in hours.

   a. 13   **b.** 14   **c.** 15   **d.** 17

18. Clara Wong worked $3\frac{1}{5}$ hours on Tuesday, $4\frac{2}{3}$ hours on Wednesday, and $2\frac{3}{4}$ hours on Friday.
Estimate the total number of hours worked.

   a. 11   **b.** 9   **c.** 12   **d.** 10

19. Bill jogged $16\frac{1}{9}$ miles on Thursday and $12\frac{7}{8}$ miles on Friday.
Estimate the difference in the number of miles.

   a. 3   **b.** 4   **c.** 5   **d.** 1

Decimals

Rounding

> **Rules:** To round a decimal, look at the digit to the right of the place to which you are rounding.
>
> **1.** If the digit is **less than 5**, round **down**.
>
> **2.** If the digit is **5 or more**, round **up**.
>
> **Examples:**
> **a.** **1**.8 rounded to the nearest whole number is **2**.
> **b.** 8.**0**5 rounded to the nearest tenth is 8.**1**.
> **c.** .7**3**8 rounded to the nearest hundredth is .7**4**.
> **d.** 4.01**8**6 rounded to the nearest thousandth is 4.01**9**.

▶ Round to the nearest whole number.

1. 2.3   **2.** 25.5   **3.** 17.82   **4.** 17.2   **5.** .69   **6.** 9.492

▶ Round to the nearest tenth.

7. 4.23   **8.** 4.65   **9.** 1.802   **10.** 7.05   **11.** .09   **12.** 8.54

▶ Round to the nearest hundredth.

13. 1.732   **14.** 2.466   **15.** 3.074   **16.** 8.027   **17.** .072   **18.** .005

▶ Round to the nearest thousandth.

19. .1234   **20.** 1.8032   **21.** .2765   **22.** 7.0052   **23.** .0718   **24.** .0009

Estimation

▶ Choose whichever gives the best estimate. Choose a, b, or c.

25. $8.40 + $9.80   **a.** $8 + $10   **b.** $9 + $9   **c.** $9 + $10

26. $68.07 − $12.96   **a.** $60 − $12   **b.** $70 − $13   **c.** $70 − $12

27. 1.9 × 12.3   **a.** 2 × 12   **b.** 2 × 13   **c.** 1 × 12

28. 58.9 ÷ 3   **a.** 60 ÷ 3   **b.** 600 ÷ 3   **c.** 51 × $\frac{1}{3}$

▶ Choose whichever gives the best estimate. Choose a, b, c, or d.

29. Andrea had a balance of $17.90 in her checking account. She deposited $196.50 and wrote a check for $38.90. Estimate her new balance.

a. $140   **b.** $150   **c.** $180   **d.** $190

30. Laura buys 2.75 meters of cloth at $4.15 per meter. Estimate the cost of the cloth.

a. $8   **b.** $12   **c.** $15   **d.** $10

Per Cent

▶ Choose whichever gives the best estimate. Choose a, b, c, or d.

1. 25% of $99
   a. 20% of $100   b. 30% of $100   c. $\frac{1}{4}$ of $100   d. $\frac{1}{4}$ of $90

2. 11% of $612
   a. 10% of $600   b. 10% of $700   c. 20% of $600   d. 20% of $700

3. 28% of $895
   a. 25% of $900   b. 25% of $800   c. 30% of $900   d. 30% of $800

4. $33\frac{1}{3}$% of $895
   a. $\frac{1}{3}$ of $900   b. 30% of $900   c. 30% of $800   d. 40% of 900

5. $12\frac{1}{2}$% of $47.50
   a. 10% of $50   b. $\frac{1}{10}$ of $50   c. $\frac{1}{8}$ of $48   d. $\frac{1}{8}$ of $50

6. $16\frac{2}{3}$% of $35.50
   a. $\frac{1}{6}$ of $36   b. 10% of $36   c. 20% of $36   d. $\frac{2}{3}$ of $36

7. Gina bought a pair of shoes for 25% off the regular price of $27.50.
   Estimate the amount she saved.
   a. $5   b. $7
   c. $9   d. $11

8. Mrs. Suarez bought a wool rug for 20% off the regular price of $251.75.
   Estimate the amount she saved.
   a. $25   b. $60   c. $50   d. $80

9. Warm-up suits are regularly priced at $41.90. Mr. Chu bought a suit at a 10% discount sale.
   Estimate the amount he saved.
   a. $10   b. $8   c. $6   d. $4

10. Hironu bought a coat for 30% off the regular price of $119.98.
    Estimate the amount he saved.
    a. $24   b. $30   c. $36   d. $40

Metric System

Units of Length

One **millimeter** is about the thickness of a dime.
One **centimeter** is about the width of a paper clip.
One **meter** is about the width of a door.
One **kilometer** is about the length of 10 football fields.

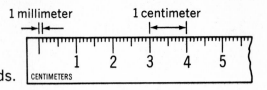

▶ Choose the metric unit you would use to measure each of the following. Choose a, b, or c.

1. The thickness of a quarter   a. millimeter   b. centimeter   c. meter

2. The length of a toothbrush   a. millimeter   b. centimeter   c. meter

3. The height of a doorknob from the floor   a. centimeter   b. kilometer   c. meter

4. The distance from New York to Dallas   a. centimeter   b. kilometer   c. meter

This table shows the units of length in the metric system.

Units of Length	Prefix	Meaning
1 millimeter (mm) = .001 meter (m)	milli–	$\frac{1}{1000}$, or .001
1 centimeter (cm) = .01 meter	centi–	$\frac{1}{100}$, or .01
1 decimeter (dm) = .1 meter	deci–	$\frac{1}{10}$, or .1
1 dekameter (dam) = 10 meter	deka–	10
1 hectometer (hm) = 100 meters	hecto–	100
1 kilometer (km) = 1000 meters	kilo–	1000

Rules: 1. To change to a smaller metric unit, multiply by 10, by 100, or by 1000, and so on.

2. To change to a larger metric unit, divide by 10, by 100, or by 1000, and so on.

▶ Complete the table. First, check whether you multiply or divide. Then check the number by which to multiply or divide. The first one is done for you.

	From	To	Multiply	Divide	By 10	By 100	By 1000
5.	kilometers	meters	✔				✔
6.	centimeters	meters					
7.	millimeters	centimeters					
8.	hectometers	meters					
9.	meters	decimeters					

▶ Choose the equivalent measure. Choose a, b, c, or d.

10. 30 meters   **a.** 3000 cm   **b.** 300 cm   **c.** 30 cm   **d.** .3 cm

11. 5 kilometers   **a.** 5 m   **b.** .5 m   **c.** 50 m   **d.** 5000 m

12. 25 centimeters   **a.** 2500 m   **b.** 250 m   **c.** 2.5 m   **d.** .25 m

13. 6376 millimeters   **a.** 6.376 dm   **b.** 63.76 dm   **c.** 637.6 dm   **d.** .6376 dm

14. 893 meters   **a.** 89.3 km   **b.** 8.93 km   **c.** .893 km   **d.** .0893 km

Units of Mass

One milligram is about the weight of the wing of a bee.

Five grams is about the weight (mass) of a nickel.

One kilogram is about the weight of a pair of shoes (adult size).

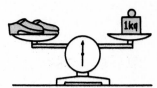

▶ Choose the metric unit you would use to give the weight of each of the following. Choose a, b, or c.

1. An automobile   **a.** milligram   **b.** gram   **c.** kilogram

2. A person   **a.** milligram   **b.** gram   **c.** kilogram

3. A slice of bread   **a.** milligram   **b.** gram   **c.** kilogram

4. One drop of water   **a.** milligram   **b.** gram   **c.** kilogram

Use this table for Exercises **5–15.**

> 1000 milligrams (mg) = 1 gram (g)
> 1000 grams = 1 kilogram (kg)
> 1000 kilograms = 1 metric ton (t)

▶ Choose the equivalent measure. Choose a, b, c, or d.

5. 800 milligrams   **a.** .8 g   **b.** .08 g   **c.** 80 g   **d.** 8 g

6. 37 grams   **a.** 3.7 kg   **b.** .37 kg   **c.** 3700 kg   **d.** .037 kg

7. 9.86 kilograms   **a.** 986 g   **b.** 9860 g   **c.** 98.6 g   **d.** 9.86 g

8. 5 metric tons   **a.** 5000 kg   **b.** 500 kg   **c.** 5 kg   **d.** .5 kg

9. 1.85 grams   **a.** 1850 mg   **b.** .185 mg   **c.** 1.85 mg   **d.** 18.5 mg

10. 40,000 kg   **a.** 400 t   **b.** 40 t   **c.** 4 t   **d.** .4 t

▶ Choose the best weight for each object. Choose a, b, c, or d.

11. A postage stamp   **a.** 20 mg   **b.** 20 g   **c.** 200 g   **d.** 2 kg

12. A large paper clip   **a.** 1 mg   **b.** 1 g   **c.** 10 g   **d.** .1 kg

13. A slice of bread   **a.** 25 mg   **b.** 25 g   **c.** 250 g   **d.** 25 kg

14. A loaf of bread   **a.** 462 mg   **b.** 462 g   **c.** 4.62 g   **d.** 1 kg

15. A basketball   **a.** 6 mg   **b.** 60 mg   **c.** 6 g   **d.** 6 kg

Units of Capacity

An eyedropper holds about 1 milliliter of liquid.
A tablespoon holds about 15 milliliters of liquid.
A drinking glass holds about 250 milliliters of liquid.
A milk carton (1-quart size) contains a little less than 1 liter.
A gasoline tank truck holds about 30 kiloliters of gasoline.

▶ Choose the metric unit you would use to measure each of the following. Choose a, b, or c.

1. A spoonful of medicine	a. milliliter	b. liter	c. kiloliter
2. A tankful of gasoline for a car	a. milliliter	b. liter	c. kiloliter
3. The water in a swimming pool	a. milliliter	b. liter	c. kiloliter
4. Drops from an eyedropper	a. milliliter	b. liter	c. kiloliter
5. Antifreeze for the radiator of a car	a. milliliter	b. liter	c. kiloliter

Use this table for Exercises **6–14.**

> 1000 milliliters (ml) = 1 liter (L)
> 1000 liters = 1 kiloliter (kL)

▶ Choose the equivalent measure. Choose a, b, c, or d.

6. 500 milliliters	a. .05 L	b. .5 L	c. 5 L	d. 50 L
7. 3 liters	a. 30 mL	b. 300 mL	c. 3000 mL	d. .3 mL
8. 457 liters	a. 4.57 kL	b. 45.7 kL	c. 4570 kL	d. .457 kL
9. 21 kiloliters	a. 21,000 L	b. 210 L	c. .21 L	d. 2.1 L
10. 37 milliliters	a. 37,000 L	b. 3.7 L	c. .037 L	d. .37 L

11. One teaspoon contains 5 milliliters.
How many teaspoons are there in a bottle that contains 250 milliliters?

12. One tablespoon contains 15 milliliters.
How many teaspoons are in one tablespoon (see Exercise 11)?

13. One tablespoon contains 15 milliliters.
How many tablespoons can be poured from a bottle that contains 510 milliliters?

14. A drinking glass contains 250 milliliters.
How many glasses can be poured from a bottle that contains 1 liter?

U.S. Measures

12 inches(in.) = 1 foot(ft.)	2 pints(pt.) = 1 quart(qt.)	60 minutes(min.) = 1 hour(hr.)
3 feet = 1 yard(yd.)	4 quarts = 1 gallon(gal.)	24 hours = 1 day
36 inches = 1 yard	16 ounces(oz.) = 1 pound(lb.)	7 days = 1 week(wk.)

▶ Use the table to add. The first one in each row is done for you.

1. 2 ft. 6 in.
  +3 ft. 9 in.
  5 ft. 15 in. = 5 ft. + 1 ft. 3 in.
  = **6 ft. 3 in.**

2. 1 ft. 7 in.
  +4 ft. 8 in.

3. 6 ft. 9 in.
  +2 ft. 9 in.

4. 3 yd. 2 ft.
  +4 yd. 2 ft.
  7 yd. 4 ft. = 7 yd. + 1 yd. 1 ft.
  = **8 yd. 1 ft.**

5. 6 yd. 2 ft.
  +9 yd. 2 ft.

6. 1 yd. 2 ft.
  +8 yd. 1 ft.

7. 4 yd. 16 in.
  +7 yd. 25 in.
  11 yd. 41 in. = 11 yd. + 1 yd. 5 in.
  = **12 yd. 5 in.**

8. 3 yd. 27 in.
  +4 yd. 30 in.

9. 5 yd. 19 in.
  +2 yd. 19 in.

10. 4 gal. 3 qt.
  +3 gal. 3 qt.
  7 gal. 6 qt. = 7 gal. + 1 gal. 2 qt.
  = **8 gal. 2 qt.**

11. 5 gal. 2 qt.
  +7 gal. 3 qt.

12. 22 gal. 3 qt.
  +47 gal. 1 qt.

13. 19 lb. 9 oz.
  +31 lb. 8 oz.
  50 lb. 17 oz. = 50 lb. + 1 lb. 1 oz.
  = **51 lb. 1 oz.**

14. 7 lb. 15 oz.
  +9 lb. 5 oz.

15. 98 lb. 10 oz.
  +97 lb. 11 oz.

16. 4 hr. 36 min.
  +9 hr. 28 min.
  13 hr. 64 min. = 13 hr. + 1 hr. 4 min.
  = **14 hr. 4 min.**

17. 2 hr. 50 min.
  +7 hr. 40 min.

18. 12 hr. 10 min.
  +18 hr. 55 min.

19.   5 wk.   8 days
        +2 wk.   6 days
   ─────────────────────
        7 wk. 14 days = 7 wk. + 2 wk.

                = **9 wk.**

20.   8 wk. 5 days
        +3 wk. 2 days
   ───────────────────

21.   1 wk. 6 days
        +4 wk. 5 days
   ───────────────────

Subtraction

▶Use the table on page 131 to subtract. The first one in each row is done for you.

1.   3 ft. 6 in.
        −2 ft. 5 in.
   ─────────────────
        1 ft. 1 in.

2.   12 ft. 9 in.
        − 9 ft. 6 in.
   ──────────────────

3.   18 ft. 11 in.
        − 8 ft. 7 in.
   ───────────────────

4.   4 ft. 1 in. =   3 ft. 13 in.
        −2 ft. 9 in.   −2 ft. 9 in.
   ────────────────────────────────
                         1 ft. 4 in.

5.   12 ft. 7 in.
        − 8 ft. 9 in.
   ──────────────────

6.   2 ft. 3 in.
        −   9 in.
   ─────────────────

7.   9 yd. 1 ft. =   8 yd. 4 ft.
        −5 yd. 2 ft.   −5 yd. 2 ft.
   ───────────────────────────────
                        3 yd. 2 ft.

8.   7 yd. 1 ft.
        −4 yd. 2 ft.
   ─────────────────

9.   3 yd. 0 ft.
        −2 yd. 1 ft.
   ─────────────────

10.   5 gal. 3 qt.
        −4 gal. 2 qt.
   ─────────────────
        1 gal. 1 qt.

11.   7 gal. 2 qt.
        −5 gal. 1 qt.
   ─────────────────

12.   10 gal. 3 qt.
        − 8 gal. 1 qt.
   ───────────────────

13.   9 gal. 2 qt. =   8 gal. 6 qt.
        −6 gal. 5 qt.   −6 gal. 5 qt.
   ─────────────────────────────────
                         2 gal. 1 qt.

14.   4 gal. 1 qt.
        −2 gal. 3 qt.
   ─────────────────

15.   7 gal. 4 qt.
        −2 gal. 6 qt.
   ─────────────────

16.   9 lb. 15 oz.
        −2 lb. 3 oz.
   ─────────────────
        7 lb. 12 oz.

17.   10 lb. 12 oz.
        − 9 lb. 5 oz.
   ───────────────────

18.   181 lb. 7 oz.
        − 10 lb. 5 oz.
   ───────────────────

19.   5 lb. 12 oz. =   4 lb. 28 oz.
        −2 lb. 13 oz.   −2 lb. 13 oz.
   ─────────────────────────────────
                         2 lb. 15 oz.

20.   8 lb. 2 oz.
        −5 lb. 4 oz.
   ────────────────

21.   9 lb. 8 oz.
        −6 lb. 9 oz.
   ────────────────

22.   11 hr. 12 min. =   10 hr. 72 min.
        − 8 hr. 40 min.   − 8 hr. 40 min.
   ──────────────────────────────────────
                            2 hr. 32 min.

23.   8 hr. 10 min.
        −4 hr. 40 min.
   ───────────────────

24.   7 hr. 15 min
        −3 hr. 45 min
   ──────────────────

25.   17 days 6 hr. =   16 days 30 hr.
        −13 days 8 hr.   −13 days 8 hr.
   ──────────────────────────────────────
                           3 days 22 hr.

26.   6 days 1 hr.
        −3 days 2 hr.
   ──────────────────

27.   9 days 5 hr.
        −6 days 8 hr.
   ──────────────────

Multiplication and Division

▶ Use the table on page 131 to multiply. The first one in each row is done for you.

1.
$$\begin{array}{r} 2 \text{ ft. } 4 \text{ in.} \\ \times 5 \\ \hline \end{array}$$

10 ft. 20 in. = 10 ft. + (<u>1 ft. 8 in.</u>)
= **11 ft. 8 in.**

2.
$$\begin{array}{r} 1 \text{ ft. } 9 \text{ in.} \\ \times 2 \\ \hline \end{array}$$

3.
$$\begin{array}{r} 5 \text{ ft. } 4 \text{ in.} \\ \times 4 \\ \hline \end{array}$$

4.
$$\begin{array}{r} 3 \text{ yd. } 2 \text{ ft.} \\ \times 7 \\ \hline \end{array}$$

21 yd. 14 ft. = 21 yd. + (<u>4 yd. 2 ft.</u>)
= **25 yd. 2 ft.**

5.
$$\begin{array}{r} 8 \text{ yd. } 1 \text{ ft.} \\ \times 7 \\ \hline \end{array}$$

6.
$$\begin{array}{r} 6 \text{ yd. } 2 \text{ ft.} \\ \times 9 \\ \hline \end{array}$$

7.
$$\begin{array}{r} 4 \text{ gal. } 3 \text{ qt.} \\ \times 5 \\ \hline \end{array}$$

20 gal. 15 qt. = 20 gal. + (<u>3 gal. 3 qt.</u>)
= **23 gal. 3 qt.**

8.
$$\begin{array}{r} 6 \text{ gal. } 2 \text{ qt.} \\ \times 9 \\ \hline \end{array}$$

9.
$$\begin{array}{r} 5 \text{ gal. } 3 \text{ qt.} \\ \times 8 \\ \hline \end{array}$$

10.
$$\begin{array}{r} 5 \text{ hr. } 35 \text{ min.} \\ \times 4 \\ \hline \end{array}$$

20 hr. 140 min. = 20 hr. + (<u>2 hr. 20 min.</u>)
= **22 hr. 20 min.**

11.
$$\begin{array}{r} 5 \text{ hr. } 12 \text{ min.} \\ \times 6 \\ \hline \end{array}$$

12.
$$\begin{array}{r} 9 \text{ hr. } 15 \text{ min.} \\ \times 8 \\ \hline \end{array}$$

▶ Divide. The first one in each row is done for you.

13. $5\overline{)6 \text{ yd. } 2 \text{ ft.}} = 5\overline{)20 \text{ ft.}}$ ⟵ 4 ft.
4 ft. = **1 yd. 1 ft.**

14. $8\overline{)2 \text{ yd. } 2 \text{ ft.}}$

15. $4\overline{)5 \text{ yd. } 1 \text{ ft.}}$

16. $2\overline{)8 \text{ gal. } 2 \text{ qt.}} = 2\overline{)34 \text{ qt.}}$ ⟵ 17 qt.
17 qt. = **4 gal. 1 qt.**

17. $2\overline{)12 \text{ gal. } 2 \text{ qt.}}$

18. $3\overline{)2 \text{ gal. } 1 \text{ qt.}}$

19. $3\overline{)16 \text{ lb. } 5 \text{ oz.}} = 3\overline{)261 \text{ oz.}}$ ⟵ 87 oz.
87 oz. = **5 lb. 7 oz.**

20. $3\overline{)16 \text{ lb. } 8 \text{ oz.}}$

21. $5\overline{)9 \text{ lb. } 6 \text{ oz.}}$

22. $5\overline{)20 \text{ days } 10 \text{ hr.}}$ ⟵ **4 days 2 hr.**

23. $6\overline{)18 \text{ days } 6 \text{ hr.}}$

24. $4\overline{)12 \text{ days } 8 \text{ hr.}}$

SAMPLE COMPETENCY TEST

Choose the correct answer. Choose a, b, c, *or* d.

1. Add: 2354
43
+ 642

   a. 2049   b. 3049

   c. 3039   d. 2939

2. Subtract: 2345
− 196

   a. 2149   b. 2251

   c. 2541   d. 2249

3. Written in words, 7.04 is

   a. seven and four tenths

   b. seven hundred four

   c. seven and four hundredths

   d. seventy-four

4. Multiply: 320
✕ 45

   a. 13,400   b. 14,400

   c. 1440   d. 8400

5. Add: 17 + 8 + 104 + 92

   a. 121   b. 221

   c. 131   d. 231

6. Which is equal to $\frac{3}{4}$?

   a. 75   b. 7.5

   c. .75   d. .075

7. Add: $1\frac{3}{7} + 2\frac{2}{7}$

   a. $3\frac{6}{7}$ b. $1\frac{5}{14}$

   c. $3\frac{6}{49}$ d. $3\frac{5}{7}$

8. How many centimeters long is this paper clip?

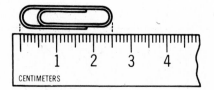

   a. 25   b. 2.4

   c. 2.5   d. .25

9. Divide: $19 \overline{)437}$

a. 33   b. 23

c. 230   d. 13

10. Which is equal to 39%?

a. $\frac{1}{3}$ b. $\frac{2}{3}$

c. $\frac{3}{10}$ d. $\frac{39}{100}$

11. Subtract: $13.04 - 7.32$

a. 6.72   b. 20.36

c. 5.72   d. 6.62

12. Which decimal has the smallest value?

a. .03   b. .073

c. .243   d. .487

13. Multiply: $\frac{3}{4} \times \frac{3}{5}$

a. $\frac{6}{9}$ b. $\frac{3}{20}$

c. $\frac{1}{20}$ d. $\frac{9}{20}$

14. Add:
$$\begin{array}{r} 2.75 \\ 4.03 \\ 6.724 \\ + 8.3 \\ \hline \end{array}$$

a. 21.804   b. 20.804

c. 20.84   d. 21.704

15. Divide: $8 \overline{)4.72}$

a. 590   b. 59

c. 5.9   d. .59

16. Subtract: $\frac{5}{6} - \frac{1}{3}$

a. $\frac{1}{2}$ b. $\frac{4}{6}$

c. $\frac{4}{3}$ d. $\frac{6}{6}$

17. Which is equal to 45%?

a. 4.5   b. .45

c. .045   d. 45

18. Multiply .25 by .06.

a. 1.20   b. .150

c. .0150   d. .1500

19. What temperature is shown on the Celsius thermometer at the right?

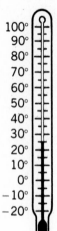

a. 20°

b. 22°

c. 30°

d. 25°

23. This spinner has 5 equal areas marked A, B, C, D, and E.
What is the probability that the pointer will stop in area C on the next spin?

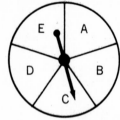

a. $\frac{5}{5}$ or 1   b. $\frac{1}{5}$

c. $\frac{3}{5}$ d. 0

20. Which is the numeral for sixty-four and twenty-three hundredths?

a. 64.23   b. 6423

c. 64 + 2300   d. 64.023

24. In lowest terms, the ratio of 16 to 48 is

a. $\frac{16}{48}$ b. $\frac{48}{16}$

c. $\frac{1}{3}$ d. $\frac{4}{12}$

21. What is 40% of 15?

a. 60   b. 9

c. 3   d. 6

25. Which is equal to 25%?

a. $\frac{1}{2}$ b. $\frac{1}{3}$

c. $\frac{1}{5}$ d. $\frac{1}{4}$

22. Divide: $8 \div \frac{1}{2}$

a. 4   b. 16

c. $\frac{1}{4}$ d. $\frac{1}{16}$

26. Divide: $2.1\overline{)3.15}$

a. 1.5   b. 150

c. 1.05   d. 15

27. What is $\frac{3}{5}$ of 80?

    a. 45   **b.** 16

    c. 240   **d.** 48

28. Solve for n: $\frac{2}{3} = \frac{n}{27}$

    a. 3   **b.** 9

    c. 6   **d.** 18

29. Which is equal to $\frac{17}{5}$?

    a. 17   **b.** $4\frac{1}{5}$

    c. $3\frac{2}{5}$ **d.** $3\frac{4}{5}$

30. The graph shows how many hours Rosa practiced the guitar during one week. On which days did she practice more than $1\frac{1}{2}$ hours?

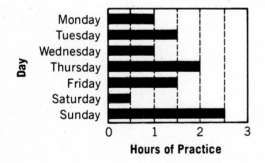

    a. Tuesday and Sunday

    b. Monday and Wednesday

    c. Saturday and Sunday

    d. Thursday and Sunday

31. What is the perimeter in meters of this triangle?

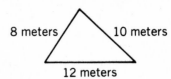

    a. 30   **b.** 54

    c. 27   **d.** 24

32. The circle graph shows how people get to work in a certain city.
How much greater is the per cent of people who drive alone to work than those who walk?

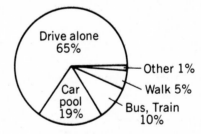

    a. 5%   **b.** 60%

    c. 70%   **d.** 14%

33. The scale on a road map is

1 centimeter = 60 kilometers.

If two towns are 5 centimeters apart on the map, what is the real distance between them in kilometers?

    a. 60   **b.** 180

    c. 300   **d.** 400

34. Pedro had a balance of $321.45 in his checking account. He wrote a check for $43.97.
What is the new balance?

a. $277.48   b. $365.42

c. $287.48   d. $276.42

35. The distance from Dallas to Phoenix is 1021 miles. The distance from Dallas to Omaha is 672 miles.
How many miles difference is there between the two distances?

a. 351   b. 1693

c. 459   d. 349

36. An average serving of ground meat is 4 ounces.
How many servings are there in 32 ounces of ground meat?

a. 4   b. 128

c. 8   d. 64

37. Use the table at the right to find the sales tax on a purchase of $1.65.

Amount of Purchase	Sales Tax
0¢-16¢	0¢
17¢-49¢	1¢
50¢-83¢	2¢
84¢-$1.16	3¢
$1.17-$1.49	4¢
$1.50-$1.83	5¢
$1.84-$2.16	6¢
$2.17-$2.49	7¢

a. 5¢

b. 2¢

c. $1.70

d. $1.75

38. Julia rode the bus to her grandparents' farm. She got on the bus at 2:20 PM, and got off the bus at 3:50 PM.
How many hours did the bus trip take?

a. $\frac{1}{2}$ b. $1\frac{1}{2}$

c. $1\frac{5}{6}$ d. $1\frac{2}{5}$

39. On a trip, Bill drove for $3\frac{1}{2}$ hours at an average speed of 82 kilometers per hour. How many kilometers did he drive? Use the formula

Distance = Rate × Time

a. 574   b. 287

c. 246   d. 41

40. How many square feet of carpet would be needed to cover the floor of a room 12 feet long and 9 feet wide?

a. 100   b. 96

c. 108   d. 42

41. Mr. Johnson wishes to buy a new car that costs $6520. The car dealer offered him $1250 for his old car.
How much will Mr. Johnson pay for the new car?

a. $5270   b. $4270

c. $5370   d. $4370

42. What is the discount?

a. $70

b. $28

c. $7

d. $42

SALE!

20% off

Regular Price
$35

47. Tina bought a new sofa. She gave the clerk $50 and made 18 monthly payments of $35 each.
What was the total cost of the sofa?

a. $480

b. $680

c. $580

d. $630

43. Harry bought $\frac{3}{4}$ pound of grapes. Laura bought $\frac{1}{2}$ pound of grapes.
How many pounds did they buy in all?

a. $\frac{3}{8}$

b. $1\frac{1}{4}$

c. $1\frac{1}{2}$

d. 1

48. The Tanaka family used 520 kilowatt hours of electricity in a month. Electricity costs $.065 per kilowatt hour. How much did they pay for electricity that month?

a. $3.38

b. $33.80

c. $31.80

d. $33.70

44. In a tournament, a team bowled games of 160, 175, 200, and 133.
What was the team's average score?

a. 142

b. 117

c. 668

d. 167

49. In a basketball game, a player took 25 shots and scored five times.
What per cent of the shots did the player make?

a. 5%

b. 25%

c. 20%

d. 15%

45. Ben wants to buy one can of beets. At which price will one can cost the least?

a. 5 for $1.54

b. 4 for $1.35

c. 3 for 99¢

d. 2 for 69¢

50. What is the volume in cubic feet of this refrigerator? Use the formula

Volume = Length × Width × Height

a. 54

b. 18

c. 15

d. 44

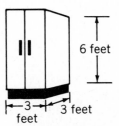

6 feet

3 feet

3 feet

46. A dinner costs $9.80. A 15% tip for the waiter is closest to

a. $2.50

b. $1.00

c. $2.00

d. $1.50

ANSWERS

Page 1   1. Survey Test

	a	b	c	d	e	f	g	h	i
1.	13	13	14	14	12	16	18	12	11
2.	23	22	20	21	23	34	46	74	165
3.	35	31	169	238	2333	5861	16,789	15,137	36,896

Page 1   2. Inventory Test

	a	b	c	d	e	f	g	h	i	j	k
1.	13	8	7	10	10	9	14	15	8	14	14
2.	9	8	12	14	8	8	10	6	9	10	9
3.	10	9	15	10	5	16	11	16	7	18	8
4.	11	13	12	15	9	13	16	12	6	12	9
5.	13	10	11	17	11	4	7	13	17	9	12
6.	11	6	15	11	10	7	13	12	14	11	12

Page 2   2A. Practice Set

	a	b	c	d	e	f	g	h	i	j	k
1.	7	7	13	9	15	15	3	16	7	14	10
2.	14	14	9	12	6	10	17	13	4	9	14
3.	11	10	10	10	5	13	9	4	12	10	10
4.	11	11	11	6	12	7	9	7	8	5	5
5.	16	9	6	11	13	8	12	7	6	6	12
6.	9	5	11	2	4	8	18	16	11	7	11
7.	13	8	13	9	6	8	10	8	12	9	17
8.	6	14	12	15	4	10	9	3	8	7	15

Page 3   3. Inventory Test

	a	b	c	d	e	f	g	h	i	j
1.	12	15	12	18	13	16	19	18	20	14
2.	18	17	17	16	17	13	17	19	15	24
3.	21	14	25	27	14	21	18	20	15	21

Page 3   3A. Practice Set

	a	b	c	d	e	f	g	h	i	j
1.	18	15	16	12	22	15	15	15	18	18
2.	17	12	19	22	20	16	18	16	17	17
3.	18	19	19	23	16	24	17	20	21	16

Page 4   4. Inventory Test

	a	b	c			a	b	c
1.	13	17	22		4.	11	13	28
2.	15	18	23		5.	17	25	25
3.	21	16	21					

4A. Practice Set

	a	b	c
1.	18	19	26
2.	19	23	22
3.	21	13	20
4.	15	22	24
5.	24	21	23
6.	16	16	25

5. Inventory Test

	a	b	c	d	e	f	g	h	i
1.	29	41	40	59	62	59	92	72	111
2.	81	45	117	61	96	68	108	137	93

5A. Practice Set

	a	b	c	d	e	f	g	h	i
1.	67	44	134	139	54	57	157	111	79
2.	60	121	54	68	118	71	96	55	101
3.	52	104	35	63	74	94	79	93	48
4.	97	102	89	110	95	96	75	111	112

6. Inventory Test

	a	b	c	d	e	f	g	h	i	j
1.	26	28	25	30	22	26	24	25	23	29
2.	37	29	33	35	32	34	31	34	39	34

6A. Practice Set

	a	b	c	d	e	f	g	h	i	j
1.	24	26	27	29	27	26	30	27	27	30
2.	29	30	29	28	32	33	34	30	26	39

7. Inventory Test

	a	b	c	d	e	f	g
1.	172	188	126	189	249	233	1963
2.	187	1352	1606	2207	2043	2105	2590

7A. Practice Set

	a	b	c	d	e	f	g
1.	135	110	251	1165	2517	1614	2921
2.	2614	1680	2645	1373	1494	2104	2695

8. Inventory Test

	a	b	c	d	e	f
1.	7893	9611	4323	11,604	14,318	3028
2.	15,108	4965	7933	4229	12,497	11,886

8A. Practice Set

	a	b	c	d	e	f
1.	1962	4347	17,212	9402	14,409	5934
2.	9028	8721	10,089	12,575	9219	6213

Page 8   Keeping Pace

1.	21	5.	1508	9.	22,879
2.	73	6.	126	10.	Royals—118
3.	183	7.	787		
4.	24	8.	10,093		

Page 8   Career Capsule

1.	$160.00	5.	$964.00	9.	$2066.00
2.	$374.00	6.	$2630.00	10.	$2689.00
3.	$248.00	7.	$2072.00	11.	$893.00
4.	$1463.00	8.	$1128.00	12.	$1080.00

Page 9   Applications

1. $3898 2. $4468 3. $5106 4. $4748 5. $6136 6. $5598
7. $255 8. $441 9. 120 centimeters 10. 152 centimeters 11. 60 inches 12. 64 inches

Page 10   9. Survey Test

	a	b	c	d	e	f	g	h
1.	0	30	27	72	42	56	24	81
2.	141	602	360	630	1872	4302	2232	2424
3.	1104	1750	3648	3741	7504	24,106	275,070	26,496

Page 10   10. Inventory Test

	a	b	c	d	e	f	g	h	i	j
1.	9	56	9	16	14	30	18	35	3	8
2.	4	72	25	0	42	49	10	40	36	24
3.	4	28	12	20	7	56	16	16	32	6
4.	12	63	63	72	21	40	6	48	36	27

Page 11   10A. Practice Set

	a	b	c	d	e	f	g	h	i	j
1.	27	12	12	27	6	28	28	14	2	9
2.	6	0	15	20	9	1	21	8	16	5
3.	18	18	32	32	25	9	8	40	15	24
4.	8	12	42	3	63	24	81	0	40	54
5.	6	20	21	6	12	7	16	24	10	64
6.	18	36	36	14	45	48	30	63	56	49
7.	8	35	35	30	3	24	16	10	18	4
8.	5	48	72	45	81	42	54	72	56	36

Page 12   11. Inventory Test

	a	b	c	d	e	f	g	h
1.	170	102	72	108	84	126	234	288
2.	581	216	270	456	678	468	396	1498
3.	512	724	369	385	585	1917	2184	3808

11A. Practice Set

	a	b	c	d	e	f	g	h
1.	135	96	192	828	144	207	729	228
2.	1561	510	392	658	1315	872	675	1032
3.	371	1375	704	1421	588	2852	520	252
4.	414	1668	4060	203	344	1398	2808	1032

12. Inventory Test

	a	b	c
1.	24	36	84
2.	36	180	120
3.	60	40	48
4.	48	36	72
5.	60	54	210

12A. Practice Set

	a	b	c
1.	48	70	90
2.	360	120	168
3.	48	72	168
4.	108	60	72
5.	378	147	108
6.	140	192	192

13. Inventory Test

	a	b	c	d	e	f	g	h
1.	345	384	952	406	1302	810	442	1204
2.	1898	2366	1175	437	1656	1584	1014	1380
3.	988	5049	4104	3354	1520	1728	6225	9216

13A. Practice Set

	a	b	c	d	e	f	g	h
1.	768	3675	648	1029	3528	850	1440	2160
2.	1701	4324	7885	4214	1610	1363	1628	1095
3.	6080	3256	3053	7636	4002	4002	1728	3520

14. Inventory Test

	a	b	c	d	e	f	g
1.	840	1820	618	728	7248	2100	5640
2.	5490	9150	4992	1110	18,814	19,776	2800
3.	2600	4896	17,818	12,300	28,240	36,938	100,000

14A. Practice Set

	a	b	c	d	e	f	g
1.	2580	1520	735	1872	2448	10,660	4100
2.	16,192	28,120	2842	2600	8970	8100	23,028
3.	5130	9888	36,800	2150	9984	23,560	53,504

15. Inventory Test

	a	b	c	d	e	f	g
1.	1296	12,735	18,304	48,000	44,895	2412	64,400
2.	132,624	254,719	93,696	232,200	18,088	978,016	22,184

15A. Practice Set

	a	b	c	d	e	f	g
1.	5049	4158	28,350	28,080	1368	3886	6968
2.	275,912	8544	233,966	336,288	777,756	102,800	611,408

Keeping Pace

1.	34	2.	293	3.	9423	4.	6858	5.	9020
6.	120,000	7.	7644	8.	58,175	9.	23,838	10.	2011

Career Capsule

1. 174 square meters 2. 96 square meters 3. 52 square centimeters 4. 7600 square centimeters
5. 185 square meters

Applications

1. 165 calories 2. 224 calories 3. 636 calories 4. 576 calories
5. 21 square meters 6. 12 square meters 7. 6 square meters 8. 30 square meters
9. 1983 10. 1978 11. 1982

16. Survey Test

	a	b	c	d	e	f	g	h
1.	3	8	9	5	10	8	9	9
2.	29	17	67	42	18	33	9	44
3.	164	77	67	51	763	124	5779	1824

17. Inventory Test

	a	b	c	d	e	f	g	h	i	j	k
1.	6	0	3	0	3	9	2	6	8	3	6
2.	4	4	0	9	4	7	9	7	9	2	7
3.	7	5	2	6	8	8	7	1	6	8	6

17A. Practice Set

	a	b	c	d	e	f	g	h	i	j	k
1.	7	9	7	8	4	7	1	5	2	9	7
2.	8	6	3	4	9	2	8	3	5	4	4
3.	9	5	9	7	6	9	6	6	7	8	3
4.	7	8	6	6	8	9	0	6	2	7	3

18. Inventory Test

	a	b	c	d	e	f	g	h	i	j
1.	13	35	36	23	9	57	19	9	49	69
2.	56	37	75	54	69	59	45	79	2	27
3.	12	6	88	64	16	29	33	22	57	27

18A. Practice Set

	a	b	c	d	e	f	g	h	i	j
1.	38	29	12	67	16	42	65	56	24	3
2.	15	63	79	39	74	39	44	14	27	85
3.	57	9	88	52	68	7	25	58	26	47

19. Inventory Test

	a	b	c	d	e	f	g	h
1.	43	44	20	9	169	81	219	79
2.	209	135	89	185	268	684	66	428
3.	3432	155	7304	212	1216	2951	2044	1824

19A. Practice Set

	a	b	c	d	e	f	g	h
1.	189	210	98	48	115	389	291	185
2.	85	43	177	97	499	202	3106	1908
3.	1212	4457	8317	5875	2526	1235	188	2948
4.	2229	7247	5512	3332	3350	1015	3087	1767

Keeping Pace

1. 34   2. 256   3. 9469   4. 688
5. 3822   6. 69,008   7. 384   8. 1581
9. 4279   10. 1140 miles, 68,400 miles

Career Capsule

1. 1 hour 55 minutes
2. 2 hours
3. 2 hours 30 minutes

Applications

1. San Francisco   2. Baltimore   3. 2934 kilometers   4. 3180 kilometers
5. 595 kilometers   6. 1129 kilometers   7. 558 square meters   8. 698 square meters
9. 2174 square meters   10. 3901 square meters   11. 6773 square meters   12. 1256 square meters
13. 4599 square meters   14. 5157 square meters

20. Survey Test

	a	b	c	d	e	f
1.	7	6	9	5	0	6
2.	63	83	63	43 r4	31	72 r1
3.	37	34 r10	21 r1	246	13 r106	176 r88

21. Inventory Test

	a	b	c	d	e	f	g
1.	6	0	7	8	0	4	5
2.	7	5	2	7	7	6	9
3.	7	3	8	4	5	6	9
4.	3	4	8	2	2	1	8
5.	3	9	9	7	9	4	6

21A. Practice Set

	a	b	c	d	e	f	g
1.	2	7	2	2	1	5	8
2.	9	6	7	5	4	8	8
3.	7	3	2	3	6	9	6
4.	6	4	0	9	3	3	9
5.	7	5	7	4	1	4	8
6.	4	7	9	9	8	6	8

22. Inventory Test

	a	b	c	d	e	f	g
1.	94	22	32	120	42	25	41
2.	182	61	93	51	51	91	78
3.	56	92	79	36	24	35	84

22A. Practice Set

	a	b	c	d	e	f
1.	45	91	156	61	25	77
2.	113	58	80	54	13	102
3.	36	27	35	312	57	65
4.	94	34	91	23	157	54

23. Inventory Test

	a	b	c	d	e	f
1.	54 r4	37 r1	91 r1	17 r2	101 r2	45 r7
2.	120 r3	26 r3	105 r1	30 r3	54 r2	13 r7
3.	49 r3	36 r3	87 r4	253 r1	44 r2	47 r1
4.	270 r5	38 r1	324 r3	98 r2	79 r3	353 r4
5.	261 r7	724	42 r3	144 r6	21 r3	901 r6
6.	99 r3	218	94 r5	86 r2	468 r3	423 r2
7.	174 r1	113 r1	77 r7	69 r2	801 r4	557 r6

23A. Practice Set

	a	b	c	d	e	f
1.	178 r1	321 r1	104 r4	152 r1	170 r1	101 r3
2.	114 r5	101 r3	71 r6	130 r4	36 r3	201 r3
3.	126 r1	142 r4	134 r2	68 r8	60 r4	30 r1
4.	133 r1	22 r6	102 r3	140 r2	33 r6	280 r2
5.	3607 r1	387 r1	531 r1	125 r3	359 r1	355 r3
6.	749 r1	353 r1	237 r1	2420 r1	215 r3	848 r1
7.	861 r1	3238	345 r1	804 r3	1316 r4	990 r3

Page 27   24. Inventory Test

	a	b	c
1.	6	14	5
2.	8	10	18
3.	6	3	3
4.	$9\frac{1}{2}$	32	40
5.	9	10	21

24A. Practice Set

	a	b	c
1.	20	3	11
2.	12	16	84
3.	3	18	98
4.	77	6	26
5.	12	30	7

Page 27   Career Capsule

1. $11,887.00   2. $82,465.00   3. $.36   4. $.53

Page 28   25. Inventory Test

	a	b	c	d	e	f
1.	31 r3	15 r5	42	81	47 r29	41
2.	281 r4	57	17	100 r30	26 r38	41 r1
3.	75	136 r20	71	54 r1	275	22 r64
4.	56	48	71 r51	123	80 r43	45

Page 28   25A. Practice Set

	a	b	c	d	e	f
1.	44 r6	71 r56	42 r3	52 r7	62	33 r12
2.	42 r11	52	258 r10	182 r15	102	125 r9
3.	98	29 r47	83	140	74 r36	258 r12
4.	157	102	110 r8	873 r6	38	246

Page 29   25B. Practice Set

	a	b	c	d	e
1.	56 r16	126 r9	182 r36	261 r40	33 r34
2.	67	36	17	13	32
3.	251	257	199	44	147
4.	115 r4	137 r1	114 r10	259 r22	198 r14

Page 29   Keeping Pace

1. 268   2. 19,408   3. 2919   4. 1108
5. 1248   6. 34,032   7. 92   8. 148 r13
9. 100 r36   10. 26

Career Capsule

1. 26 hours   4. 62 hours
2. 36 hours   5. 25 hours
3. 23 hours   6. 34 hours

Page 30   Applications

1. 12 hours   2. 10 hours   3. 8 hours   4. 2 hours   5. 15 hours   6. 20 hours
7. 2 hours   8. 19 hours   9. 8 hours   10. 12 hours   11. 2 hours   12. 17 hr. 12 min.
13. 3 for 29¢   14. 4 for 49¢   15. 10 for 99¢   16. 6 for 99¢   17. 12 for 89¢   18. 8 for 69¢

Pages 31-33   Review of Applications: Whole Numbers

1. a	2. d	3. b	4. c
5. b	6. c	7. b	8. d
9. d	10. b	11. c	12. d
13. d	14. a	15. d	16. a
17. d	18. d	19. b	20. d
21. a	22. a	23. d	24. a
25. b	26. c		

Page 34   Review of Skills: Whole Numbers

			[1]7	2			[2]1	[3]2	
[4]1	[5]7	0		[6]1	9	2	4		
[7]4	7		[8]5	[9]2	5				
	2		[10]1	0		[11]1	2	[12]1	
[13]9	[14]9	[15]2			[16]7	8		5	
[17]8		[18]3	5		[19]2	2	[20]8		
[21]5	0	6		[22]1	[23]5		5		
			[24]2	4	[25]2		[26]2	[27]4	
[28]4	[29]8	2	5		4		[30]6	6	
[31]9	8		[32]1	8					

Page 35   26. Survey Test

1. a $\frac{3}{6}$ or $\frac{1}{2}$ b $\frac{5}{9}$ 2. (a), (c), (d)
3. a 18   b 21   4. a $\frac{1}{4}$ b $\frac{3}{4}$
5. a $\frac{26}{3}$ b $\frac{61}{8}$ c $\frac{24}{4}$ 6. a $8\frac{1}{2}$ b $2\frac{2}{3}$ c $2\frac{2}{5}$

27. Inventory Test

1. $\frac{5}{8}$ 2. $\frac{2}{6}$ or $\frac{1}{3}$ 3. $\frac{5}{12}$ 4. $\frac{2}{3}$
5. $\frac{3}{5}$ 6. $\frac{1}{4}$ 7. $\frac{3}{8}$ 8. $\frac{11}{16}$

Page 36   27A. Practice Set

1. $\frac{3}{4}$ 2. $\frac{4}{8}$ or $\frac{1}{2}$ 3. $\frac{7}{16}$ 4. $\frac{1}{8}$
5. $\frac{5}{6}$ 6. $\frac{3}{8}$ 7. $\frac{2}{5}$ 8. $\frac{11}{24}$

Page 36   28. Inventory Test

	a	b	c	d	e
1.	Equivalent	Not equivalent	Equivalent	Not equivalent	Not equivalent
2.	Equivalent	Not equivalent	Equivalent	Equivalent	Not equivalent
3.	Equivalent	Not equivalent	Equivalent	Equivalent	Not equivalent

Page 37   28A. Practice Set

	a	b	c	d	e
1.	Equivalent	Equivalent	Equivalent	Equivalent	Not equivalent
2.	Equivalent	Not equivalent	Equivalent	Not equivalent	Equivalent
3.	Equivalent	Not equivalent	Not equivalent	Equivalent	Equivalent

Page 37   29. Inventory Test

	a	b	c	d	e
1.	$\frac{3}{6}$	$\frac{8}{12}$	$\frac{6}{30}$	$\frac{12}{16}$	$\frac{10}{16}$
2.	$\frac{10}{15}$	$\frac{6}{48}$	$\frac{18}{24}$	$\frac{30}{36}$	$\frac{9}{24}$
3.	$\frac{16}{20}$	$\frac{35}{40}$	$\frac{15}{25}$	$\frac{4}{32}$	$\frac{9}{27}$
4.	$\frac{21}{48}$	$\frac{20}{36}$	$\frac{24}{34}$	$\frac{70}{100}$	$\frac{18}{42}$

Page 38   29A. Practice Set

	a	b	c	d	e
1.	$\frac{6}{8}$	$\frac{4}{6}$	$\frac{15}{24}$	$\frac{12}{36}$	$\frac{2}{32}$
2.	$\frac{15}{36}$	$\frac{12}{32}$	$\frac{20}{45}$	$\frac{21}{42}$	$\frac{21}{35}$
3.	$\frac{12}{21}$	$\frac{9}{33}$	$\frac{35}{42}$	$\frac{12}{18}$	$\frac{28}{48}$
4.	$\frac{14}{32}$	$\frac{5}{60}$	$\frac{27}{72}$	$\frac{20}{100}$	$\frac{55}{99}$

30. Inventory Test

	a	b	c	d	e	f	g	h
1.	$\frac{1}{2}$	$\frac{2}{3}$	$\frac{3}{8}$	$\frac{2}{3}$	$\frac{1}{2}$	$\frac{1}{4}$	$\frac{1}{3}$	$\frac{2}{3}$
2.	$\frac{2}{5}$	$\frac{1}{3}$	$\frac{4}{5}$	$\frac{5}{6}$	$\frac{1}{6}$	$\frac{5}{7}$	$\frac{1}{6}$	$\frac{1}{8}$
3.	$\frac{2}{3}$	$\frac{1}{2}$	$\frac{5}{8}$	$\frac{5}{9}$	$\frac{7}{12}$	$\frac{7}{8}$	$\frac{1}{4}$	$\frac{1}{5}$
4.	$\frac{1}{2}$	$\frac{10}{11}$	$\frac{1}{3}$	$\frac{3}{8}$	$\frac{3}{5}$	$\frac{3}{10}$	$\frac{5}{8}$	$\frac{1}{2}$

Page 39   30A. Practice Set

	a	b	c	d	e	f	g	h
1.	$\frac{1}{2}$	$\frac{1}{4}$	$\frac{5}{7}$	$\frac{2}{3}$	$\frac{3}{5}$	$\frac{3}{4}$	$\frac{1}{6}$	$\frac{1}{2}$
2.	$\frac{1}{3}$	$\frac{8}{9}$	$\frac{1}{3}$	$\frac{3}{4}$	$\frac{3}{5}$	$\frac{1}{5}$	$\frac{1}{5}$	$\frac{3}{5}$
3.	$\frac{10}{13}$	$\frac{1}{7}$	$\frac{1}{2}$	$\frac{1}{8}$	$\frac{1}{4}$	$\frac{7}{8}$	$\frac{2}{3}$	$\frac{3}{8}$
4.	$\frac{1}{3}$	$\frac{5}{11}$	$\frac{8}{27}$	$\frac{1}{6}$	$\frac{1}{10}$	$\frac{2}{5}$	$\frac{1}{4}$	$\frac{2}{5}$

Page 39   31. Inventory Test

	a	b	c	d
1.	$\frac{5}{2}$	$\frac{13}{4}$	$\frac{7}{4}$	$\frac{14}{3}$
2.	$\frac{8}{3}$	$\frac{8}{2}$	$\frac{21}{4}$	$\frac{15}{2}$
3.	$\frac{18}{3}$	$\frac{31}{8}$	$\frac{51}{8}$	$\frac{30}{6}$
4.	$\frac{23}{5}$	$\frac{32}{16}$	$\frac{67}{16}$	$\frac{17}{6}$

Page 40   31A. Practice Set

	a	b	c	d
1.	$\frac{9}{4}$	$\frac{15}{6}$	$\frac{21}{8}$	$\frac{17}{16}$
2.	$\frac{33}{4}$	$\frac{28}{5}$	$\frac{51}{16}$	$\frac{14}{2}$
3.	$\frac{17}{3}$	$\frac{43}{6}$	$\frac{39}{4}$	$\frac{45}{16}$
4.	$\frac{85}{12}$	$\frac{14}{7}$	$\frac{44}{5}$	$\frac{61}{5}$

Career Capsule

1. $3\frac{1}{3}$ hours   4. $5\frac{1}{2}$ hours   7. $8\frac{1}{2}$ hours
2. $3\frac{3}{4}$ hours   5. $4\frac{3}{4}$ hours   8. $7\frac{1}{4}$ hours
3. $4\frac{5}{6}$ hours   6. $5\frac{5}{12}$ hours   9. $8\frac{1}{3}$ hours

Page 41   32. Inventory Test

	a	b	c	d	e	f	g	h
1.	2	4	4	$5\frac{1}{3}$	$6\frac{1}{4}$	$2\frac{1}{2}$	$2\frac{1}{3}$	$2\frac{2}{5}$
2.	5	$2\frac{2}{3}$	$2\frac{1}{4}$	$1\frac{1}{4}$	$1\frac{3}{4}$	6	$3\frac{1}{5}$	6
3.	$1\frac{1}{2}$	$7\frac{1}{2}$	$3\frac{2}{5}$	$2\frac{1}{6}$	$1\frac{1}{8}$	3	$2\frac{5}{7}$	$3\frac{1}{2}$
4.	$1\frac{1}{12}$	$1\frac{1}{8}$	$1\frac{7}{9}$	$1\frac{1}{4}$	$1\frac{1}{6}$	2	$5\frac{1}{2}$	3
5.	$1\frac{4}{5}$	$4\frac{2}{3}$	$1\frac{10}{11}$	5	$2\frac{3}{8}$	$4\frac{3}{10}$	$7\frac{1}{4}$	$8\frac{1}{3}$

Page 41   32A. Practice Set

	a	b	c	d	e	f	g	h
1.	1	$1\frac{3}{5}$	$1\frac{5}{7}$	3	$1\frac{1}{11}$	$2\frac{3}{4}$	$5\frac{2}{5}$	$3\frac{1}{3}$
2.	$1\frac{2}{3}$	$3\frac{1}{4}$	$5\frac{2}{3}$	$2\frac{1}{8}$	5	$3\frac{3}{5}$	$1\frac{2}{15}$	$2\frac{1}{3}$
3.	$4\frac{1}{6}$	$2\frac{5}{8}$	$4\frac{1}{2}$	$1\frac{6}{17}$	$2\frac{2}{7}$	4	$2\frac{1}{2}$	$1\frac{1}{5}$
4.	$3\frac{5}{6}$	5	$3\frac{1}{4}$	$4\frac{2}{7}$	$4\frac{1}{3}$	$2\frac{2}{3}$	$3\frac{1}{5}$	$1\frac{3}{5}$
5.	$5\frac{6}{7}$	$1\frac{2}{17}$	$4\frac{1}{8}$	$25\frac{1}{2}$	1	$1\frac{1}{3}$	2	$7\frac{4}{5}$

Page 42   **Keeping Pace**   **Career Capsule**

1. 13,582
2. 46,020
3. 197 r4
4. 3892
5. $\frac{4}{10}$ or $\frac{2}{5}$

6. $\frac{15}{45}$
7. a $\frac{4}{5}$ b $\frac{2}{5}$
8. a $2\frac{1}{2}$ b $6\frac{1}{4}$
9. $\frac{39}{8}$
10. $\frac{5}{8}, \frac{31}{48}, \frac{2}{3}, \frac{11}{16}, \frac{17}{24}, \frac{3}{4}$

1. 90°
2. 120°
3. 45°

Page 43   **33. Survey Test**

	a	b	c	d	e	f	g
1.	$\frac{3}{4}$	$\frac{2}{3}$	$1\frac{2}{3}$	$\frac{5}{6}$	$1\frac{3}{8}$	$1\frac{5}{12}$	$1\frac{17}{24}$
2.	$1\frac{13}{24}$	$1\frac{3}{16}$	$1\frac{31}{40}$	$1\frac{23}{48}$	$8\frac{7}{24}$	$10\frac{11}{12}$	$13\frac{15}{16}$
3.	$1\frac{1}{12}$	$2\frac{7}{24}$	$6\frac{13}{36}$				

Page 43   **34. Inventory Test**

	a	b	c	d	e	f	g
1.	$\frac{3}{4}$	$\frac{4}{5}$	1	$1\frac{1}{3}$	$1\frac{1}{2}$	2	$1\frac{3}{8}$
2.	6	7	$9\frac{1}{2}$	$15\frac{1}{4}$	$4\frac{3}{4}$	$6\frac{1}{2}$	$6\frac{1}{7}$

Page 44   **34A. Practice Set**

	a	b	c			a	b	c
1.	$1\frac{1}{4}$	$\frac{5}{8}$	$1\frac{2}{3}$		4.	$1\frac{1}{4}$	$\frac{7}{10}$	$3\frac{4}{5}$
2.	$1\frac{1}{3}$	$1\frac{1}{12}$	$7\frac{3}{4}$		5.	$1\frac{1}{4}$	$7\frac{5}{8}$	$8\frac{9}{16}$
3.	$\frac{6}{7}$	$1\frac{1}{9}$	$\frac{10}{11}$					

Page 44   **35. Inventory Test**

1. a 1, 2, 4, 8   b 1, 7   c 1, 2, 4, 8, 16   d 1, 5, 25   e 1, 2, 3, 4, 6, 12
   f 1, 2, 3, 4, 6, 9, 12, 18, 36   g 1, 2, 4, 5, 8, 10, 20, 40   h 1, 41
2. a 1, 3, 5, 15   b 1, 17   c 1, 2, 4, 8, 16, 32, 64   d 1, 2, 3, 4, 6, 8, 9, 12, 18, 24, 36, 72
   e 1, 2, 4, 5, 8, 10, 16, 20, 40, 80   f 1, 3, 9, 27   g 1, 3   h 1, 2, 13, 26
3. a 1, 2, 5, 10, 25, 50   b 1, 2, 4, 8, 16, 32   c 1, 2, 7, 14   d 1, 2, 3, 6, 9, 18   e 1, 37
   f 1, 2, 3, 4, 6, 8, 9, 12, 16, 18, 24, 36, 48, 72, 144   g 1, 2, 3, 4, 6, 9, 12, 18, 27, 36, 54, 108
   h 1, 2, 4, 5, 8, 10, 20, 25, 40, 50, 100, 200

Page 44   **35A. Practice Set**

1. a 1, 5, 7, 35   b 1, 2, 3, 5, 6, 10, 15, 30   c 1, 2, 4, 5, 10, 20   d 1, 2, 4, 11, 22, 44
   e 1, 2, 3, 6   f 1, 13   g 1, 3, 9   h 1, 2, 3, 6, 7, 14, 21, 42
2. a 1, 2, 3, 6, 9, 18, 27, 54   b 1, 2, 11, 22   c 1, 2, 7, 14, 49, 98
   d 1, 2, 4, 5, 10, 20, 25, 50, 100   e 1, 2, 4, 7, 14, 28   f 1, 2, 3, 4, 6, 8, 12, 16, 24, 48
   g 1, 2, 4, 7, 8, 14, 28, 56   h 1, 3, 9, 27, 81
3. a 1, 3, 11, 33   b 1, 29   c 1, 2, 3, 4, 5, 6, 8, 10, 12, 15, 20, 24, 30, 40, 60, 120
   d 1, 5, 25, 125   e 1, 3, 5, 15, 25, 75   f 1, 2, 3, 4, 5, 6, 10, 12, 15, 20, 30, 60
   g 1, 3, 17, 51   h 1, 2, 3, 4, 6, 8, 9, 12, 16, 18, 24, 32, 36, 48, 72, 96, 144, 288
4. a 1, 2, 4, 13, 26, 52   b 1, 2, 3, 4, 6, 7, 12, 14, 21, 28, 42, 84
   c 1, 2, 3, 4, 6, 8, 12, 16, 24, 32, 48, 96   d 1, 2, 4, 8, 11, 22, 44, 88
   e 1, 2, 5, 7, 10, 14, 35, 70   f 1, 97   g 1, 2, 3, 4, 6, 8, 9, 12, 18, 24, 27, 36, 54, 72, 108, 216
   h 1, 2, 4, 5, 8, 10, 16, 20, 32, 40, 80, 160

36. Inventory Test

	a	b	c	d	e	f	g
1.	8	9	12	18	60	35	40
2.	12	15	24	20	15	14	16
3.	20	10	42	36	48	40	25

36A. Practice Set

	a	b	c	d	e	f	g
1.	20	24	21	18	15	30	45
2.	72	16	36	75	36	48	30
3.	36	30	22	30	35	63	24
4.	96	38	36	125	72	144	48

37. Inventory Test

	a	b	c	d	e	f	g
1.	$6; \frac{2}{6}, \frac{1}{6}$	$4; \frac{2}{4}, \frac{3}{4}$	$6; \frac{4}{6}, \frac{1}{6}$	$8; \frac{5}{8}, \frac{2}{8}$	$12; \frac{2}{12}, \frac{9}{12}$	$8; \frac{1}{8}, \frac{4}{8}$	$15; \frac{10}{15}, \frac{3}{15}$
2.	$12; \frac{7}{12}, \frac{9}{12}$	$24; \frac{16}{24}, \frac{3}{24}$	$12; \frac{3}{12}, \frac{4}{12}$	$21; \frac{9}{21}, \frac{7}{21}$	$16; \frac{6}{16}, \frac{7}{16}$	$20; \frac{15}{20}, \frac{8}{20}$	$48; \frac{3}{48}, \frac{16}{48}$
3.	$16; \frac{3}{16}, \frac{4}{16}$	$10; \frac{3}{10}, \frac{4}{10}$	$30; \frac{25}{30}, \frac{4}{30}$	$14; \frac{4}{14}, \frac{7}{14}$	$30; \frac{9}{30}, \frac{14}{30}$	$24; \frac{5}{24}, \frac{9}{24}$	$60; \frac{42}{60}, \frac{35}{60}$

37A. Practice Set

	a	b	c	d	e	f	g
1.	$8; \frac{5}{8}, \frac{6}{8}$	$10; \frac{6}{10}, \frac{5}{10}$	$12; \frac{9}{12}, \frac{8}{12}$	$24; \frac{3}{24}, \frac{20}{24}$	$10; \frac{3}{10}, \frac{8}{10}$	$12; \frac{2}{12}, \frac{3}{12}$	$24; \frac{21}{24}, \frac{2}{24}$
2.	$16; \frac{3}{16}, \frac{8}{16}$	$24; \frac{14}{24}, \frac{15}{24}$	$24; \frac{16}{24}, \frac{21}{24}$	$48; \frac{15}{48}, \frac{16}{48}$	$40; \frac{15}{40}, \frac{32}{40}$	$21; \frac{14}{21}, \frac{6}{21}$	$10; \frac{2}{10}, \frac{7}{10}$
3.	$32; \frac{12}{32}, \frac{7}{32}$	$20; \frac{8}{20}, \frac{5}{20}$	$40; \frac{35}{40}, \frac{4}{40}$	$120; \frac{25}{120}, \frac{24}{120}$	$100; \frac{30}{100}, \frac{7}{100}$	$24; \frac{21}{24}, \frac{10}{24}$	$16; \frac{3}{16}, \frac{10}{16}$

Career Capsule

1. 1 inch   2. $2\frac{5}{8}$ inches   3. $1\frac{1}{8}$ inches   4. $1\frac{3}{8}$ inches   5. $2\frac{1}{2}$ inches   6. $1\frac{1}{8}$ inches

38. Inventory Test

	a	b	c	d	e	f	g
1.	$1\frac{1}{4}$	$\frac{7}{8}$	$1\frac{5}{12}$	$\frac{11}{16}$	$1\frac{1}{12}$	$1\frac{1}{8}$	$1\frac{1}{2}$
2.	$1\frac{3}{16}$	$4\frac{1}{10}$	$1\frac{7}{12}$	$6\frac{7}{16}$	$1\frac{1}{20}$	$9\frac{1}{12}$	$9\frac{11}{16}$

38A. Practice Set

	a	b	c	d	e	f	g
1.	$\frac{1}{2}$	$\frac{3}{4}$	$\frac{17}{24}$	$1\frac{1}{16}$	$\frac{47}{48}$	$1\frac{13}{24}$	$\frac{7}{18}$
2.	$\frac{13}{16}$	$1\frac{1}{14}$	$1\frac{2}{9}$	$\frac{31}{40}$	$1\frac{27}{40}$	$1\frac{5}{48}$	$1\frac{1}{16}$
3.	$6\frac{1}{2}$	$6\frac{1}{2}$	$9\frac{1}{3}$	$3\frac{13}{16}$	$10\frac{13}{30}$	$9\frac{5}{8}$	$7\frac{62}{63}$

38B. Practice Set

	a	b	c	d
1.	$\frac{11}{12}$	$\frac{19}{20}$	$\frac{13}{16}$	$\frac{4}{9}$
2.	$1\frac{1}{16}$	$1\frac{5}{24}$	$1\frac{7}{12}$	$8\frac{7}{24}$
3.	$1\frac{9}{40}$	$1\frac{7}{24}$	$\frac{17}{24}$	$9\frac{13}{28}$

39. Inventory Test

	a	b	c	d	e	f	g
1.	2	$1\frac{1}{8}$	$2\frac{7}{24}$	$1\frac{5}{24}$	$1\frac{3}{20}$	$1\frac{7}{18}$	$1\frac{7}{16}$
2.	$1\frac{11}{12}$	$1\frac{2}{3}$	$1\frac{11}{12}$	$1\frac{2}{7}$	$8\frac{7}{24}$	$10\frac{9}{16}$	$7\frac{19}{24}$

39A. Practice Set

	a	b	c	d	e	f	g
1.	$1\frac{7}{12}$	$1\frac{1}{5}$	$1\frac{17}{48}$	$1\frac{6}{7}$	$1\frac{8}{15}$	$1\frac{13}{16}$	$1\frac{13}{24}$
2.	$1\frac{1}{6}$	$1\frac{7}{24}$	$2\frac{5}{18}$	$1\frac{11}{16}$	$1\frac{11}{24}$	$\frac{7}{10}$	$1\frac{7}{16}$
3.	$7\frac{5}{24}$	$8\frac{23}{30}$	$5\frac{5}{16}$	$7\frac{17}{24}$	$8\frac{8}{15}$	$15\frac{5}{48}$	$8\frac{7}{60}$
4.	$6\frac{47}{48}$	$10\frac{13}{20}$	$15\frac{7}{15}$	7	$5\frac{23}{24}$	$7\frac{11}{12}$	$19\frac{1}{2}$
5.	$7\frac{2}{3}$	$10\frac{13}{16}$	$10\frac{1}{18}$	$6\frac{1}{36}$	$13\frac{5}{8}$	$7\frac{14}{15}$	$13\frac{19}{20}$

39B. Practice Set

	a	b	c
1.	$2\frac{1}{8}$	1	$1\frac{31}{36}$
2.	$1\frac{5}{6}$	$1\frac{4}{21}$	$1\frac{19}{50}$
3.	$1\frac{15}{16}$	$8\frac{5}{16}$	$14\frac{13}{15}$
4.	$1\frac{7}{18}$	$1\frac{17}{48}$	$8\frac{41}{60}$
5.	$\frac{27}{32}$	$10\frac{23}{60}$	$12\frac{1}{6}$

Keeping Pace

1. 20,158
2. 2789
3. 45,076
4. 169
5. $1\frac{5}{24}$
6. $\frac{4}{5}$
7. $\frac{36}{39}$
8. 120
9. $1\frac{19}{48}$
10. $10\frac{11}{15}$

Applications

1. 12 hours
2. $12\frac{1}{4}$ hours
3. $8\frac{1}{6}$ hours
4. $2\frac{3}{4}$ hours
5. $10\frac{7}{10}$ hours
6. $11\frac{1}{2}$ hours
7. $12\frac{1}{2}$ hours
8. $8\frac{7}{10}$ hours
9. $6\frac{1}{2}$ hours
10. $9\frac{7}{20}$ hours

40. Survey Test

	a	b	c	d	e	f	g	h				
1.	$\frac{1}{2}$	$\frac{1}{4}$	$\frac{1}{8}$	$\frac{1}{16}$	$\frac{5}{12}$	$\frac{11}{24}$	$\frac{3}{20}$	$\frac{7}{24}$	3.	$\frac{5}{24}$	5.	$1\frac{3}{4}$
2.	$\frac{7}{30}$	$\frac{5}{48}$	$1\frac{7}{24}$	$3\frac{1}{2}$	$5\frac{1}{4}$	$6\frac{7}{16}$	$1\frac{5}{6}$	$5\frac{29}{40}$	4.	$\frac{5}{24}$	6.	$3\frac{1}{8}$

41. Inventory Test

	a	b	c	d	e	f	g	h
1.	$\frac{1}{4}$	$\frac{1}{3}$	$\frac{1}{2}$	$\frac{1}{4}$	$\frac{4}{7}$	$\frac{3}{11}$	$\frac{7}{8}$	$\frac{1}{2}$
2.	$1\frac{2}{3}$	$2\frac{1}{2}$	$1\frac{3}{8}$	$5\frac{1}{2}$	$3\frac{1}{3}$	$2\frac{3}{5}$	$2\frac{1}{6}$	$4\frac{1}{3}$

41A. Practice Set

	a	b	c	d
1.	$\frac{1}{6}$	$\frac{1}{6}$	$\frac{1}{2}$	$\frac{4}{5}$
2.	$\frac{3}{4}$	$1\frac{1}{4}$	$\frac{3}{8}$	$3\frac{5}{8}$

Page 52 — **42. Inventory Test**

	a	b	c	d	e	f	g	h
1.	$\frac{5}{8}$	$\frac{1}{2}$	$\frac{11}{16}$	$\frac{1}{4}$	$\frac{1}{12}$	$\frac{29}{48}$	$\frac{1}{3}$	$\frac{5}{16}$
2.	$\frac{2}{3}$	$\frac{13}{24}$	$\frac{3}{40}$	$\frac{7}{24}$	$1\frac{1}{3}$	$2\frac{7}{20}$	$1\frac{13}{80}$	$5\frac{5}{48}$

Page 52 — **42A. Practice Set**

	a	b	c	d	e	f	g	h
1.	$\frac{7}{20}$	$\frac{11}{16}$	$\frac{1}{6}$	$\frac{7}{20}$	$\frac{9}{32}$	$\frac{5}{24}$	$\frac{17}{48}$	$\frac{1}{60}$
2.	$\frac{2}{21}$	$\frac{5}{16}$	$\frac{5}{48}$	$\frac{5}{24}$	$\frac{1}{20}$	$\frac{13}{32}$	$\frac{1}{7}$	$\frac{1}{2}$
3.	$2\frac{13}{24}$	$5\frac{1}{12}$	$2\frac{3}{16}$	$2\frac{1}{4}$	$5\frac{11}{60}$	$1\frac{3}{16}$	$2\frac{13}{20}$	$1\frac{11}{48}$

Page 53 — **43. Inventory Test**

	a	b	c	d	e	f	g
1.	$3\frac{5}{12}$	$4\frac{1}{6}$	$2\frac{3}{4}$	$3\frac{5}{6}$	$\frac{13}{24}$	$\frac{1}{8}$	$\frac{11}{18}$
2.	$\frac{15}{16}$	$1\frac{13}{24}$	$4\frac{1}{2}$	$6\frac{9}{16}$	$5\frac{3}{16}$	$1\frac{13}{20}$	$\frac{13}{16}$

Page 53 — **43A. Practice Set**

	a	b	c	d	e	f	g
1.	$2\frac{5}{6}$	$\frac{17}{24}$	$1\frac{11}{16}$	$1\frac{11}{12}$	$\frac{19}{20}$	$5\frac{2}{9}$	$\frac{19}{24}$
2.	$1\frac{5}{12}$	$2\frac{1}{2}$	$4\frac{1}{6}$	$5\frac{15}{16}$	$6\frac{11}{24}$	$\frac{5}{8}$	$1\frac{11}{16}$
3.	$1\frac{1}{3}$	$1\frac{11}{30}$	$1\frac{7}{8}$	$1\frac{4}{5}$	$4\frac{1}{20}$	$4\frac{13}{15}$	$4\frac{7}{24}$

Page 54 — **Keeping Pace**

1. 22,676   2. 237   3. 195,082   4. 160 r5   5. $2\frac{5}{48}$
6. $\frac{7}{9}$ 7. $5\frac{7}{8}$ 8. $5\frac{1}{6}$ 9. $17\frac{19}{24}$ 10. $\frac{5}{48}$

Page 54 — **Applications**

1. $\frac{1}{3}$ hour   2. $1\frac{1}{3}$ hours   3. $2\frac{3}{8}$ hours   4. $\frac{1}{6}$ hour   5. $1\frac{1}{6}$ hours
6. $1\frac{1}{24}$ hours   7. $15\frac{1}{4}$ miles   8. $16\frac{1}{4}$ miles   9. $\frac{1}{4}$ mile   10. $\frac{1}{2}$ mile
11. $\frac{1}{4}$ mile   12. $\frac{1}{2}$ mile

Page 55 — **44. Survey Test**

	a	b	c	d
1.	$2\frac{1}{3}$	15	$\frac{8}{15}$	$\frac{2}{5}$
2.	4	360	$3\frac{1}{8}$	$17\frac{1}{2}$
3.	$\frac{3}{4}$	$\frac{1}{4}$	$1\frac{1}{2}$	2440

45. Inventory Test

	a	b	c	d
1.	$\frac{1}{6}$	$\frac{3}{16}$	$\frac{5}{12}$	$\frac{12}{25}$
2.	$\frac{5}{16}$	$\frac{3}{20}$	$\frac{1}{9}$	$\frac{1}{4}$

45A. Practice Set

	a	b	c	d
1.	$\frac{5}{12}$	$\frac{1}{4}$	$\frac{1}{14}$	$\frac{5}{24}$
2.	$\frac{3}{5}$	$\frac{1}{8}$	$\frac{1}{16}$	$\frac{8}{15}$

Page 56 — **46. Inventory Test**

	a	b	c	d
1.	$\frac{4}{9}$	$\frac{7}{12}$	$\frac{4}{25}$	$\frac{3}{8}$
2.	$\frac{3}{20}$	$\frac{1}{10}$	$\frac{9}{14}$	$\frac{1}{4}$
3.	$\frac{3}{40}$	$\frac{15}{32}$	$\frac{7}{48}$	$\frac{3}{8}$
4.	$\frac{3}{5}$	$\frac{3}{5}$	$\frac{3}{20}$	$\frac{5}{16}$
5.	$\frac{2}{3}$	$\frac{3}{4}$	$\frac{5}{8}$	$\frac{1}{4}$

46A. Practice Set

	a	b	c	d
1.	$\frac{2}{5}$	$\frac{3}{14}$	$\frac{24}{35}$	$\frac{1}{8}$
2.	$\frac{2}{9}$	$\frac{1}{2}$	$\frac{25}{48}$	$\frac{3}{8}$
3.	$\frac{3}{16}$	$\frac{7}{22}$	$\frac{2}{25}$	$\frac{11}{32}$
4.	$\frac{1}{4}$	$\frac{1}{3}$	$\frac{11}{16}$	$\frac{1}{40}$
5.	$\frac{1}{15}$	$\frac{3}{10}$	$\frac{7}{15}$	$\frac{2}{5}$

Page 57   47. Inventory Test   47A. Practice Set

	a	b	c	d		a	b	c	d
1.	$\frac{1}{4}$	$\frac{1}{2}$	$1\frac{1}{6}$	10	1.	$\frac{7}{20}$	$6\frac{2}{3}$	$\frac{1}{3}$	$\frac{3}{40}$
2.	12	10	$\frac{1}{6}$	3	2.	$\frac{2}{3}$	1	$2\frac{1}{10}$	$\frac{2}{3}$
3.	$\frac{7}{20}$	$\frac{1}{8}$	$\frac{3}{5}$	$\frac{1}{8}$	3.	$\frac{1}{3}$	$3\frac{3}{10}$	$\frac{9}{16}$	$\frac{5}{8}$
4.	$\frac{3}{5}$	$\frac{3}{4}$	$13\frac{1}{2}$	$13\frac{1}{2}$	4.	$4\frac{1}{2}$	$\frac{5}{8}$	6	$22\frac{1}{2}$

Page 58   48. Inventory Test   48A. Practice Set

	a	b	c	d		a	b	c	d
1.	$\frac{5}{6}$	$\frac{1}{2}$	$2\frac{3}{4}$	$15\frac{1}{6}$	1.	2	$2\frac{2}{5}$	$\frac{15}{32}$	2
2.	$\frac{15}{16}$	27	$\frac{3}{4}$	$\frac{7}{10}$	2.	110	$6\frac{7}{8}$	80	$16\frac{1}{3}$
3.	$3\frac{3}{4}$	$8\frac{1}{6}$	1	$3\frac{3}{20}$	3.	$4\frac{1}{8}$	$1\frac{9}{16}$	$1\frac{1}{3}$	$38\frac{1}{2}$
4.	18	3	15	18	4.	$6\frac{2}{3}$	30	$3\frac{1}{30}$	$2\frac{4}{5}$
					5.	6	$10\frac{1}{2}$	$5\frac{1}{4}$	18
					6.	$10\frac{5}{12}$	$7\frac{7}{8}$	$6\frac{7}{8}$	$28\frac{1}{2}$

Page 59   49. Inventory Test   49A. Practice Set

	a	b	c	d		a	b	c	d
1.	120	675	660	312	1.	215	441	481	450
2.	459	1596	1995	3621	2.	488	539	335	621
					3.	1225	715	1180	1673

Page 60   50. Inventory Test   50A. Practice Set

	a	b	c		a	b	c
1.	$\frac{1}{5}$	$\frac{1}{6}$	$11\frac{55}{64}$	1.	$\frac{1}{3}$	$\frac{1}{4}$	$8\frac{4}{5}$
2.	$3\frac{3}{4}$	$2\frac{3}{5}$	$5\frac{1}{3}$	2.	$\frac{7}{8}$	$1\frac{7}{9}$	$\frac{1}{3}$
3.	$\frac{1}{12}$	5	9	3.	$\frac{1}{2}$	3	$4\frac{13}{16}$
				4.	$\frac{147}{512}$	$1\frac{17}{64}$	$\frac{68}{75}$

Page 60   Keeping Pace   Career Capsule

1. 181,586   2. 3206   3. 82,344   4. 110 r48   5. $10\frac{1}{24}$ 1. $53\frac{1}{2}$ inches
6. $\frac{4}{7}$ 7. 600   8. $4\frac{1}{3}$ 9. $2\frac{7}{8}$ 10. 4   2. Yes

Page 61   Applications

1. 52 cubic feet   2. $239\frac{1}{5}$ cubic yards   3. $46\frac{4}{5}$ cubic feet   4. $2595\frac{21}{25}$ cubic in.
5. 64 kilometers   6. $102\frac{1}{2}$ kilometers   7. $387\frac{1}{2}$ kilometers   8. 100 kilometers
9. 765 kilometers   10. 432 kilometers

Page 62   51. Survey Test

	a	b	c	d	e	f	g	h
1.	3	$\frac{6}{4}$	$\frac{5}{11}$	$\frac{1}{21}$	$\frac{1}{6}$	$\frac{3}{7}$	$\frac{4}{19}$	$\frac{9}{14}$
2.	16	$\frac{1}{2}$	$5\frac{1}{2}$	$2\frac{1}{2}$				
3.	$2\frac{2}{5}$	$\frac{15}{16}$	$1\frac{1}{3}$	2				
4.	$\frac{2}{3}$	16	$\frac{1}{8}$	$1\frac{5}{16}$				
5.	10	$\frac{1}{18}$	32	$\frac{1}{28}$	$\frac{2}{3}$	$\frac{5}{17}$	$1\frac{3}{4}$	$\frac{15}{41}$

Page 62 — 52. Inventory Test

	a	b	c	d	e	f	g	h
1.	$\frac{8}{7}$	$\frac{3}{2}$	$\frac{3}{7}$	$\frac{2}{5}$	2	$\frac{1}{5}$	$\frac{10}{3}$	$\frac{4}{9}$
2.	3	$\frac{1}{7}$	$\frac{25}{16}$	1	$\frac{3}{10}$	$\frac{4}{7}$	$\frac{1}{8}$	20

Page 63 — 52A. Practice Set

	a	b	c	d	e	f	g
1.	$\frac{2}{3}$	$\frac{7}{9}$	$\frac{16}{7}$	$\frac{1}{3}$	9	$\frac{4}{5}$	$\frac{7}{8}$
2.	$\frac{15}{9}$	$\frac{8}{29}$	$\frac{5}{9}$	$\frac{16}{37}$	$\frac{8}{39}$	$\frac{16}{49}$	$\frac{8}{15}$

Page 63 — 53. Inventory Test

	a	b	c	d			a	b	c	d
1.	$1\frac{1}{4}$	15	$\frac{3}{20}$	$\frac{1}{10}$		4.	$10\frac{1}{2}$	3	$1\frac{1}{5}$	$\frac{3}{5}$
2.	10	$\frac{1}{2}$	$\frac{5}{48}$	$\frac{3}{4}$		5.	$\frac{4}{5}$	5	$\frac{11}{16}$	$1\frac{3}{4}$
3.	4	$\frac{5}{6}$	$\frac{1}{10}$	$\frac{1}{12}$		6.	$3\frac{1}{5}$	$\frac{1}{30}$	12	$\frac{3}{16}$

Page 64 — 53A. Practice Set

	a	b	c	d
1.	$\frac{4}{9}$	$\frac{7}{36}$	$\frac{1}{16}$	$\frac{5}{12}$
2.	1	6	5	$\frac{8}{15}$
3.	25	$\frac{1}{32}$	21	$\frac{1}{4}$
4.	$\frac{1}{18}$	10	$2\frac{2}{5}$	4
5.	2	$\frac{3}{16}$	$\frac{1}{6}$	$\frac{1}{14}$
6.	$\frac{1}{2}$	$\frac{3}{32}$	$\frac{1}{2}$	$\frac{1}{6}$

54. Inventory Test

	a	b	c	d
1.	36	6	$\frac{6}{25}$	$\frac{5}{6}$
2.	$\frac{7}{8}$	$5\frac{5}{8}$	$1\frac{3}{11}$	$3\frac{3}{5}$
3.	$\frac{3}{4}$	$5\frac{2}{3}$	$\frac{1}{7}$	$\frac{4}{11}$
4.	$10\frac{2}{3}$	$1\frac{1}{2}$	$1\frac{6}{11}$	$1\frac{1}{2}$
5.	$\frac{8}{15}$	$2\frac{1}{2}$	$\frac{3}{20}$	20
6.	$\frac{1}{7}$	5	$4\frac{1}{6}$	6

Page 65 — 54A. Practice Set

	a	b	c	d
1.	$\frac{3}{5}$	$3\frac{3}{8}$	$1\frac{1}{2}$	$\frac{9}{50}$
2.	$4\frac{1}{2}$	$\frac{4}{9}$	$\frac{1}{3}$	$3\frac{5}{6}$
3.	$7\frac{1}{6}$	$\frac{5}{6}$	$1\frac{4}{5}$	44
4.	$5\frac{3}{5}$	14	$1\frac{17}{21}$	$5\frac{1}{2}$
5.	$\frac{7}{18}$	$1\frac{5}{16}$	$\frac{7}{15}$	$1\frac{1}{3}$
6.	$3\frac{1}{5}$	$\frac{3}{10}$	7	4

54B. Practice Set

	a	b	c	d
1.	6	5	$3\frac{1}{5}$	$\frac{7}{50}$
2.	$\frac{2}{3}$	18	$\frac{1}{4}$	$1\frac{4}{7}$
3.	$1\frac{4}{7}$	2	6	$\frac{7}{12}$
4.	$4\frac{3}{8}$	$2\frac{3}{10}$	$\frac{3}{85}$	$\frac{5}{8}$
5.	$1\frac{2}{3}$	$\frac{1}{25}$	$1\frac{1}{8}$	$4\frac{1}{2}$

Career Capsule

1. 8 feet
2. $6\frac{1}{2}$ feet
3. $\frac{49}{66}$ yard

Page 66 — 55. Inventory Test

	a	b	c	d	e	f	g
1.	12	18	28	25	$\frac{1}{18}$	$\frac{1}{15}$	$\frac{1}{15}$
2.	$1\frac{1}{3}$	14	$3\frac{3}{5}$	$\frac{1}{10}$	$1\frac{1}{5}$	$\frac{5}{6}$	$\frac{3}{14}$

Page 66 — 55A. Practice Set

	a	b	c	d	e	f	g
1.	27	40	$\frac{5}{6}$	$\frac{1}{30}$	$\frac{1}{50}$	$\frac{1}{64}$	$\frac{1}{112}$
2.	2	30	81	$\frac{1}{40}$	$\frac{5}{12}$	$\frac{1}{8}$	$1\frac{3}{5}$
3.	$3\frac{1}{3}$	42	4	2	65	$2\frac{2}{3}$	$\frac{5}{108}$

Page 67		Keeping Pace				Page 67		Applications		

Page 67 **Keeping Pace**

1. 130,798
2. 74,958
3. 3808
4. 114 r33

5. $8\frac{7}{16}$
6. $25\frac{2}{3}$
7. $3\frac{23}{24}$
8. $5\frac{1}{2}$

9. $2\frac{1}{3}$
10. $1\frac{3}{4}$

Page 67 **Applications**

1. 16
2. 10
3. 18
4. 16

5. 14
6. $4\frac{1}{2}$
7. 10
8. 32

9. 5
10. 9

Pages 68-70 **Review of Applications: Fractions**

1. a   2. d   3. b   4. c   5. b   6. a   7. d   8. c   9. a
10. d   11. b   12. b   13. d   14. a   15. c   16. c   17. c   18. d
19. c   20. d   21. b   22. d   23. a   24. b   25. a   26. c

Page 71 **Review of Skills: Whole Numbers and Fractions**

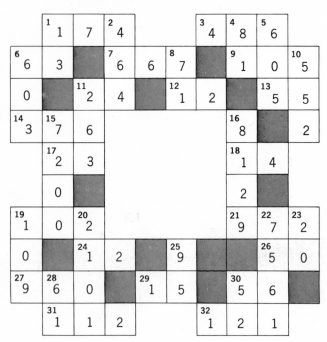

Page 72 **56. Survey Test**

1. a   twenty-eight hundredths
   b   forty-eight thousandths
   c   three and seven tenths
   d   eighty-two thousand, seven hundred ninety-five
   e   two million, five hundred thousand
2. a   25.07   b   .205
3. a   .83, .832, .9
   b   .715, 7.15, 71.5
   c   .003, .02, .2

Page 73 **57. Inventory Test**

1. a   four tenths   b   three hundred eighty-six   c   twelve thousand, three hundred twenty-four   d   six hundred fifty-eight thousand, three hundred two   e   two thousand seven hundred ninety-three ten-thousandths
2. a   thirty-eight hundredths   b   two hundred sixty-two thousandths   c   six and two hundred seventy-one thousandths   d   forty-eight thousand, nine hundred   e   eighty and eight thousandths
3. a   two hundredths   b   forty-eight and five tenths   c   seventy-eight thousandths   d   two hundred seventy-six and thirty seven hundredths   e   forty-two thousand, six hundred thirty-one
4. a   seventy-six and four tenths   b   seventy-five hundredths   c   two hundred sixty-nine thousandths   d   nine thousand two hundred sixty-four ten-thousandths   e   seven thousand two hundred five ten-thousandths
5. a   eighteen hundredths   b   twenty-five thousandths   c   forty-eight and seventeen hundredths   d   one hundred thousand   e   five million, eight hundred fifty-seven thousand, two hundred

57A. Practice Set

1. **a** four hundred sixty-one thousandths   **b** twenty-nine thousand, three hundred sixty-eight   **c** eighty thousand, six   **d** seven hundred eighty-five thousand   **e** forty-five ten-thousandths

2. **a** three and seventy-two hundredths   **b** seventeen and sixty-three hundredths   **c** three thousand   **d** two and forty-three hundredths   **e** eight million, six hundred thousand, sixty

3. **a** eight tenths   **b** eight hundred ninety-four thousandths   **c** five hundred twenty-seven ten-thousandths   **d** twenty-seven and eighty-three hundredths   **e** three hundred sixty-eight and two hundred seventy-three thousandths

4. **a** nine hundred twenty   **b** three thousandths   **c** forty-eight thousand, nine hundred forty   **d** sixty-five thousandths   **e** five thousand six hundred twenty-three ten-thousandths

5. **a** four and seventy-eight hundredths   **b** nine and seven hundred seven thousandths   **c** two thousand one hundred twenty-one ten-thousandths   **d** one and one thousandth   **e** nine and five thousand six hundred twenty-three ten-thousandths

58. Inventory Test   **58A. Practice Set**

	a	b
1.	.7	46,090
2.	12,000	.035
3.	.012	.0205
4.	8.16	8,000,040
5.	3205	6.02

	a	b
1.	.008	.0005
2.	2,500,000	28,002
3.	100.01	10.050
4.	.162	.0916
5.	.0018	50,030,000
6.	285,000	.00004

59. Inventory Test

	a	b	c
1.	.065, .6, .63	.04, .048, .05	.49, .4956, .5
2.	.481, .5, .52	.575, .58, 2	.02, .024, .2
3.	.2, .22, .222	.3, .303, .31	.6, .66, .666
4.	.026, .2, .25	.62, .6319, .633	.7, .72, .762
5.	.8, .81, .8321	.848, .85, 8.4	.063, .36, .46

59A. Practice Set

	a	b	c
1.	.083, .8, .83	.25, 2.5, 25	.027, .2702, 2.7
2.	.908, .959, .994	.426, .48, .482	.008, .07, .08
3.	7, 7.12, 7.2	.04, .05, .051	.01, .185, 1
4.	.025, .2, .25	.56, .561, 1	6.274, 6.3, 6.36
5.	.956, .96, 9.6	.9, .91, .923	.10, .11, 10.0011
6.	.085, .85, 8.5	.0401, .042, .4	.3, .32, .33
7.	.009, .02, .1	.0054, .03, .045	.0938, .097, .3

Keeping Pace

1. 159,716	**2.** 36,443	**3.** 61,028	**4.** 48	**5.** $14\frac{9}{16}$
6. $5\frac{5}{12}$	**7.** 400	**8.** $\frac{27}{72}$	**9.** .064, .61, .623	**10.** 107.5 miles

Career Capsule

1. A	**2.** G	**3.** B	**4.** D
5. H	**6.** E	**7.** C	**8.** F

60. Survey Test

	a	b	c	d	e	f
1.	5.14	56.2	2.881	19.587	1221.6	30.33
2.	17.8	.178	.735	176.5	3.50	1.237
3.	26.50	4.09	42.828			
4.	36.6	4.326	941.5			

61. Inventory Test

	a	b	c	d	e	f	g
1.	16.6	34.5	45.3	58.1	5.89	138.6	67.15
2.	38.2	17.5	57.3	113.5	2.351	85.10	14.187

61A. Practice Set

	a	b	c	d	e	f	g
1.	30.08	10.526	86.19	2.322	16.922	69.84	9.438
2.	11.824	567.6	67.95	2.1050	136.98	593.8	13.032

62. Inventory Test

	a	b	c	d	e	f	g
1.	6.24	2.07	.25	2.10	2.49	8.4	.081
2.	.392	5.09	7.25	.185	5.57	10.6	6.081
3.	3.88	.22	2.081	52.8	8.8	1.978	2.513

Page 78   62A. Practice Set   **62B. Practice Set**   **Keeping Pace**

	a	b	c		a	b				
1.	2.1	8.8	.74	**1.**	7.9	98.04	**1.**	132,688	**6.**	$1\frac{11}{48}$
2.	6.8	8.3	.25	**2.**	30.4	54.4	**2.**	16,262	**7.**	$3\frac{7}{8}$
3.	5.34	.864	6.6	**3.**	11.84	12.129	**3.**	1081	**8.**	61.026
4.	2.96	12.4	14.2	**4.**	2.586	6.040	**4.**	103	**9.**	146.9
5.	2.6	90.7	80.8	**5.**	118.4	1560.47	**5.**	464	**10.**	a 29.64
				6.	13.1	6.70				b 1786.5
				7.	9.88	3.774				

Applications

1. $88.10	**2.** $143.45	**3.** $159.01	**4.** $384.50
5. $176.40	**6.** $374.20	**7.** $162.67	**8.** $48.00

63. Survey Test

	a	b	c	d	e	f	g
1.	2.4	.54	24.5	9.00	1.100	.00286	168.0
2.	92.64	.00252	9.000	30.10	.0234	5.0076	36.60

64. Inventory Test

	a	b	c	d	e	f	g	h
1.	20.8	59.5	8.28	144.8	123.0	2.844	12.84	45.85
2.	.469	15.12	88.4	57.60	93.0	47.7	539.4	49.50
3.	150.42	2.407	670.44	41.04	10.578	514.02	1811.2	.216

64A. Practice Set

	a	b	c	d	e	f	g	h
1.	98.4	9.28	164.5	3.91	34.68	.240	98.42	590.4
2.	29.76	1621.2	204.92	4.300	60.72	1.550	193.50	183.96
3.	1732.5	729.8	.324	33.75	166.08	2710.0	364.8	2186.22

65. Inventory Test

	a	b	c	d	e	f	g
1.	2.76	2.72	.216	.312	2.016	.1650	3.06
2.	5.642	.348	.216	3.975	12.00	2.08	.4000
3.	.1653	1.116	27.74	.2968	2.520	25.2	2.376

65A. Practice Set

	a	b	c	d	e	f	g
1.	4.20	.800	5.58	35.00	2.448	57.12	1.40
2.	53.82	1.824	3.485	.7220	.3528	101.16	.5177
3.	3.2175	6.300	19.2	.5907	65.0	36.09	16.800
4.	343.68	17.16	34.56	1.17	1860	11.83	9.486

66. Inventory Test

	a	b	c	d	e	f	g
1.	.0455	.192	.090	.5880	12.00	.00090	.0256
2.	.0368	.3450	96.8	.0065	.0351	5.92	36.500

66A. Practice Set

	a	b	c	d	e	f	g
1.	.2412	7.56	.00108	.0300	12.038	.00036	.5080
2.	72.58	.00625	.0630	250.00	.01884	.00072	11.154
3.	93.025	.00072	.1419	82.07	.0182	2.665	.4221
4.	50.000	.06748	12.900	23.870	85.000	2.070	4.300

Page 83 — Keeping Pace

1. 120,766	2. 59,185	3. 75	4. $14\frac{29}{30}$	5. $1\frac{1}{2}$
6. 1.349	7. 1725	8. .7749	9. six and thirty-five thousandths	10. $17.50

Page 83 — Career Capsule

1. $.65 2. $3.80 3. $9.65 4. $18.40

Page 84 — Applications

1. $7.50	2. $8.00	3. $5.25	4. $11.00	5. $8.60
6. $86.00	7. $60.20	8. $111.80	9. 40 cubic meters	10. 80 cubic meters
11. 78 cubic meters	12. 99 cubic meters	13. 50 cubic meters		

Page 85

67. Survey Test

	a	b	c	d	e
1.	.6	.03	3.7	.326	.21
2.	1730	.63	4.8	23	.0042
3.	62.5	3.2	2.3	.2	.6

68. Inventory Test

	a	b	c	d	e	f
1.	10.8	.13	2.36	8.2	43.4	.72
2.	3.45	3.12	.248	2.76	8.64	1.29
3.	.182	.3369	7.8	9.36	3.93	.323

Page 86 — 68A. Practice Set

	a	b	c	d	e	f
1.	.63	6.3	8.72	7.56	10.8	.608
2.	.85	1.32	.86	2.08	6.9	8.5
3.	.908	.63	.12	.431	.3156	8.96
4.	3.45	87.2	9.36	.602	.1224	43.2

Page 86

69. Inventory Test

	a	b	c	d	e
1.	1.8	2.43	4.3	9.0	.346
2.	.24	.56	.22	12.3	2.9
3.	8.3	.11	.156	1.7	2.8

69A. Practice Set

	a	b	c	d	e
1.	.28	.25	.59	24.7	6.2
2.	.41	2.1	.453	.96	.14
3.	.73	5.9	7.5	.74	3.5
4.	4.33	.15	.109	6.2	.47
5.	.41	3.9	.43	1.8	6.7

Page 87 — 70. Inventory Test

	a	b	c	d	e
1.	40.2	3.1	.6	.83	5.4
2.	17.3	23	10.4	1.5	4.6
3.	.17	51	12.2	3.3	.55

Page 88

70A. Practice Set

	a	b	c	d	e
1.	3.8	2.1	.31	9.2	49
2.	17.3	.12	1.12	2.7	4.02
3.	2.9	3.41	48	36.7	.16

70B. Practice Set

	a	b	c	d	e
1.	.527	9.1	27	406	2.1
2.	140.4	.44	6.3	13.7	46
3.	1.7	30.6	3.902	20.6	4.3

Page 89 71. Inventory Test   71A. Practice Set

	a	b	c	d	e
1.	820	.62	2300	.072	86,400
2.	420	2760	.0358	.375	1080
3.	25,000	.45	14.2	.032	.013

	a	b	c	d	e
1.	.014	32.25	530	17.47	3200
2.	480	.0058	9.6	13	50
3.	.034	49.6	.0842	.2	.024

Page 90 72. Inventory Test   72A. Practice Set

	a	b	c	d	e
1.	2.5	3.4	3.6	297.6	4.3
2.	.88	45.52	260.11	1.66	7.68

	a	b	c	d	e
1.	21.6	2.9	3.4	31.7	.0
2.	13.87	1.45	.63	7.82	.01
3.	.042	6.545	1.760	.076	2.973

Page 91   73. Inventory Test

	a	b	c	d	e	f	g	h
1.	.75	$.66\frac{2}{3}$	.05	.7	$.08\frac{1}{3}$	.16	.25	.875
2.	.3125	$.16\frac{2}{3}$	.28	.06	.125	$.55\frac{5}{9}$	.27	$.28\frac{4}{7}$
3.	.045	.4	.37	.375	$.83\frac{1}{3}$	$.41\frac{2}{3}$	.36	.9

Page 91   73A. Practice Set

	a	b	c	d	e	f	g	h
1.	.15	.30	$.06\frac{1}{4}$	.80	.20	$.17\frac{1}{2}$	.55	.10
2.	$.27\frac{3}{11}$	$.05\frac{1}{2}$	.48	$.71\frac{3}{7}$	$.56\frac{1}{4}$	.68	$.91\frac{2}{3}$	$.42\frac{6}{7}$
3.	.32	.07	$.02\frac{9}{10}$	.95	$.18\frac{2}{11}$	$.77\frac{7}{9}$	.48	$.07\frac{1}{2}$

Page 92   Keeping Pace   Career Capsule

1. 97,495   2. 60,840   3. 8.4   4. $12\frac{4}{15}$ 1. 24   4. 24
5. .5625   6. $\frac{1}{5}$ 7. $4\frac{1}{9}$ 8. 31.38   2. 48   5. 12
9. .01638   10. 450   3. 12   6. 48

Page 93   Applications

1. $.485 or 48.5¢   2. $.485 or 48.5¢   3. $.415 or 41.5¢   4. $.004 or .4¢
5. $.158 or 15.8¢   6. $.485 or 48.5¢   7. $.745 or 74.5¢   8. $.77 or 77¢
9. $.192 or 19.2¢   10. $.205 or 20.5¢   11. 8   12. 36
13. 7.2 centimeters   14. 8.7 centimeters   15. 11.8 centimeters   16. 2.1 centimeters

Pages 94-96   Review of Applications: Decimals

1. b   2. a   3. c   4. a   5. c   6. a
7. a   8. a   9. d   10. b   11. a   12. d
13. c   14. a   15. d   16. a   17. c   18. c
19. d   20. b   21. d   22. a   23. d   24. a
25. d   26. c

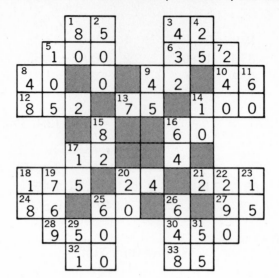

Page 98   **74. Survey Test**

	a	b	c	d
1.	$\frac{2}{1}$	$\frac{1}{3}$	$\frac{9}{4}$	$\frac{3}{4}$
2.	$\frac{15}{24}$	$\frac{12}{18}$	$\frac{3}{4}$	$\frac{48}{4}$
3.	$\frac{3}{5}$			

75. Inventory Test

	a	b	c	d
1.	$\frac{1}{2}$	$\frac{3}{1}$	$\frac{1}{3}$	$\frac{2}{1}$
2.	$\frac{4}{1}$	$\frac{2}{3}$	$\frac{4}{3}$	$\frac{2}{9}$
3.	$\frac{3}{5}$	$\frac{1}{2}$	$\frac{3}{2}$	$\frac{2}{3}$

Page 99   **75A. Practice Set**

	a	b	c	d
1.	$\frac{1}{2}$	$\frac{3}{4}$	$\frac{5}{16}$	$\frac{2}{3}$
2.	$\frac{9}{1}$	$\frac{2}{1}$	$\frac{9}{10}$	$\frac{10}{3}$
3.	$\frac{2}{1}$	$\frac{3}{2}$	$\frac{5}{2}$	$\frac{3}{10}$
4.	$\frac{1}{2}$	$\frac{5}{2}$	$\frac{1}{3}$	$\frac{18}{11}$
5.	$\frac{3}{1}$	$\frac{2}{5}$	$\frac{3}{2}$	$\frac{3}{1}$
6.	$\frac{6}{1}$	$\frac{2}{5}$	$\frac{1}{3}$	$\frac{3}{2}$
7.	$\frac{1}{2}$	$\frac{1}{3}$	$\frac{27}{19}$	$\frac{11}{4}$

76. Inventory Test

	a	b	c	d
1.	8	15	45	8
2.	10	6	90	4
3.	15	64	80	7

Page 100   **76A. Practice Set**

	a	b	c	d
1.	12	20	4	1
2.	80	30	30	30
3.	3	30	42	3

Keeping Pace

1. 61.2
2. 6.780
3. 15.98
4. .04
5. 22
6. $15\frac{1}{12}$
7. $3\frac{1}{3}$
8. $2\frac{1}{4}$
9. 72
10. 22

Career Capsule

1. $\frac{2}{1}$
2. $\frac{3}{1}$
3. $\frac{5}{2}$
4. $\frac{2}{5}$
5. $\frac{8}{9}$
6. $\frac{9}{22}$

Page 101   **Applications**

1. $\frac{1}{25}$ 2. $\frac{1}{15}$ 3. $\frac{1}{2}$ 4. $\frac{5}{7}$
5. $\frac{3}{4}$ 6. $\frac{8}{5}$ 7. $\frac{1}{20}$ 8. $\frac{1}{700}$
9. $\frac{7}{4}$ 10. 10 kilometers   11. 15 kilometers   12. 20 kilometers
13. 30 kilometers   14. 12.5 kilometers   15. 16.5 kilometers   16. 15.5 kilometers
17. 14.5 kilometers

77. Survey Test

	a	b	c	d	e	f
1.	.60, $\frac{3}{5}$	.375, $\frac{3}{8}$	.75, $\frac{3}{4}$	.08, $\frac{2}{25}$	.075, $\frac{3}{40}$	.66$\frac{2}{3}$, $\frac{2}{3}$
2.	30%	49$\frac{1}{2}$%	62$\frac{1}{2}$%	33$\frac{1}{3}$%	6$\frac{1}{2}$%	50%
	28%	80%	7%	11$\frac{1}{9}$%	25%	16%
3.	48	430	10			
	347.2	33$\frac{1}{3}$%	66$\frac{2}{3}$%			

78. Inventory Test

	a	b	c	d
1.	75%	12$\frac{1}{2}$%	48%	87$\frac{1}{2}$%
2.	42%	33$\frac{1}{3}$%	5%	62%

	a	b	c	d	e	f
3.	$\frac{2}{5}$	$\frac{19}{50}$	$\frac{9}{20}$	$\frac{13}{200}$	$\frac{3}{5}$	$\frac{3}{40}$
4.	$\frac{2}{3}$	$\frac{5}{8}$	$\frac{3}{100}$	$\frac{1}{6}$	$\frac{23}{25}$	$\frac{1}{100}$

78A. Practice Set

	a	b	c	d
1.	43%	35%	1%	4$\frac{1}{2}$%
2.	2.6%	3$\frac{1}{2}$%	28%	.7%

	a	b	c	d	e	f
3.	$\frac{9}{100}$	$\frac{1}{40}$	$\frac{73}{1000}$	$\frac{19}{25}$	$\frac{7}{8}$	$\frac{3}{200}$
4.	$\frac{3}{10}$	$\frac{17}{20}$	$\frac{1}{25}$	$\frac{19}{250}$	$\frac{1}{3}$	$\frac{3}{20}$

79. Inventory Test

	a	b	c	d	e	f
1.	.80, $\frac{4}{5}$	.44, $\frac{11}{25}$	.33$\frac{1}{3}$, $\frac{1}{3}$	.66$\frac{2}{3}$, $\frac{2}{3}$	.125, $\frac{1}{8}$	.67, $\frac{67}{100}$
2.	.75, $\frac{3}{4}$	.27, $\frac{27}{100}$	.85, $\frac{17}{20}$	.015, $\frac{3}{200}$	.45, $\frac{9}{20}$	.24, $\frac{6}{25}$
3.	.52, $\frac{13}{25}$	.63, $\frac{63}{100}$	.05, $\frac{1}{20}$	.075, $\frac{3}{40}$	.16$\frac{2}{3}$, $\frac{1}{6}$	.175, $\frac{7}{40}$

79A. Practice Set

	a	b	c	d	e	f
1.	.70, $\frac{7}{10}$	.04, $\frac{1}{25}$	.83$\frac{1}{3}$, $\frac{5}{6}$	.035, $\frac{7}{200}$	.76, $\frac{19}{25}$	.08$\frac{1}{3}$, $\frac{1}{12}$
2.	.50, $\frac{1}{2}$	.49, $\frac{49}{100}$	.20, $\frac{1}{5}$	.01, $\frac{1}{100}$	.35, $\frac{7}{20}$	.25, $\frac{1}{4}$
3.	.36, $\frac{9}{25}$	.11$\frac{1}{9}$, $\frac{1}{9}$	.095, $\frac{19}{200}$	.005, $\frac{1}{200}$	.08, $\frac{2}{25}$	.97, $\frac{97}{100}$
4.	.375, $\frac{3}{8}$	.875, $\frac{7}{8}$	.12, $\frac{3}{25}$	.55, $\frac{11}{20}$	.135, $\frac{27}{200}$	.19, $\frac{19}{100}$
5.	.46, $\frac{23}{50}$	.60, $\frac{3}{5}$	.10, $\frac{1}{10}$	.15, $\frac{3}{20}$	.0425, $\frac{17}{400}$	.54, $\frac{27}{50}$

80. Inventory Test   80A. Practice Set

	a	b	c		a	b	c
1.	12.00	24.00	450.00	1.	162.00	660.00	741.00
2.	27.00	54.00	18.00	2.	20.90	31.20	84.00
3.	13.50	25.00	266.00	3.	108.00	24.30	320.00
4.	46.80	44.10	14.40	4.	350.40	384.00	273.00
5.	9.00	630.00	510.00	5.	210.00	.76	33.60
6.	41.40	240.00	60.00				

Page 106   81. Inventory Test

	a	b	c
1.	18	25.5	32
2.	32	480	56
3.	180	344	49
4.	11	120	16
5.	630	471	270

81A. Practice Set

	a	b	c
1.	420	315	640
2.	720	630	39
3.	26	1000	378
4.	70	150	111
5.	12	291	89.2
6.	350	75	525

Page 107   82. Inventory Test

	a	b	c
1.	19.5	170	14.85
2.	120	6	15
3.	48	15	162
4.	249.1	204	2.5

82A. Practice Set

	a	b	c
1.	255	30	100
2.	250	432	84
3.	216	5.7	22.5
4.	241	125	44

Career Capsule

1.	$5700.00
2.	$3.80

Page 108   Applications

1.	$9.00	2.	$8.80	3.	$87.50	4.	$44.00
5.	$1.60	6.	$2.40	7.	$5.60	8.	$4.00
9.	$2.40	10.	$4.80	11.	$3.60	12.	$8.40
13.	4,690,000 tons	14.	6,030,000 tons	15.	19,430,000 tons	16.	32,160,000 tons

Page 109   83. Inventory Test

	a	b	c	d	e	f
1.	60%	75%	$87\frac{1}{2}$%	50%	25%	75%
2.	$33\frac{1}{3}$%	20%	20%	25%	$16\frac{2}{3}$%	$37\frac{1}{2}$%

Page 109   83A. Practice Set

	a	b	c	d	e	f
1.	75%	70%	$83\frac{1}{3}$%	25%	$37\frac{1}{2}$%	30%
2.	$87\frac{1}{2}$%	20%	32%	$66\frac{2}{3}$%	$66\frac{2}{3}$%	8%
3.	$62\frac{1}{2}$%	$16\frac{2}{3}$%	$37\frac{1}{2}$%	$31\frac{1}{4}$%	$42\frac{6}{7}$%	12%

Page 110   84. Inventory Test

	a	b	c
1.	50%	$62\frac{1}{2}$%	75%
2.	25%	50%	40%
3.	20%	30%	$33\frac{1}{3}$%
4.	30%	$62\frac{1}{2}$%	25%

84A. Practice Set

	a	b	c
1.	20%	25%	25%
2.	$37\frac{1}{2}$%	25%	$83\frac{1}{3}$%
3.	50%	$37\frac{1}{2}$%	$33\frac{1}{3}$%
4.	$16\frac{2}{3}$%	20%	10%
5.	75%	30%	64%

Page 111   85. Inventory Test

	a	b	c
1.	16	160	15.5
2.	19.2	$33\frac{1}{3}\%$	75%
3.	$33\frac{1}{3}\%$	72%	62.5%
4.	22%	210	48

85A. Practice Set

	a	b	c
1.	$16\frac{2}{3}\%$	10%	136
2.	19.8	40.5	25%
3.	15%	240	$87\frac{1}{2}\%$
4.	6%	450	28%
5.	180	80%	20%

Page 112   Keeping Pace

1. 159,075
2. 31.175
3. $12\frac{1}{24}$
4. 310
5. 1224
6. $\frac{5}{9}$
7. 600
8. $37\frac{1}{2}\%$
9. $\frac{1}{2}$
10. $42.00

Applications

1. $\frac{1}{8}$, $12\frac{1}{2}\%$
2. $\frac{1}{2}$, 50%
3. $\frac{0}{8} = 0$, 0%
4. $\frac{8}{8} = 1$, 100%
5. $\frac{1}{4}$, 25%
6. $\frac{3}{8}$, $37\frac{1}{2}\%$
7. $\frac{1}{10}$, 10%

Page 113   86. Survey Test

	a	b	c	d	e
1.	175%	263%	450%	$237\frac{1}{2}\%$	400%
2.	1.50, $1\frac{1}{2}$	2.00, 2	2.20, $2\frac{1}{5}$	4.125, $4\frac{1}{8}$	1.28, $1\frac{7}{25}$
3.	102	30%	40	150%	

87. Inventory Test

	a	b	c
1.	24	36	50
2.	96	72	64
3.	72	30	60
4.	20	25	56

Page 114   87A. Practice Set

	a	b	c
1.	400	42	90
2.	250	20	192
3.	50	1200	160
4.	52	72	200

Page 114   88. Inventory Test

	a	b	c	d	e	f	g
1.	125%	225%	160%	450%	225%	127%	300%
2.	250%	$133\frac{1}{3}\%$	175%	675%	$312\frac{1}{2}\%$	305%	350%
3.	1.25, $1\frac{1}{4}$	1.00, 1	2.50, $2\frac{1}{2}$	8.20, $8\frac{1}{5}$	2.00, 2	5.25, $5\frac{1}{4}$	2.45, $2\frac{9}{20}$
4.	2.15, $2\frac{3}{20}$	3.75, $3\frac{3}{4}$	4.125, $4\frac{1}{8}$	1.70, $1\frac{7}{10}$	1.875, $1\frac{7}{8}$	1.20, $1\frac{1}{5}$	8.00, 8

Page 115   88A. Practice Set

	a	b	c	d	e	f	g
1.	150%	325%	$166\frac{2}{3}\%$	550%	400%	372%	140%
2.	250%	$187\frac{1}{2}\%$	280%	$412\frac{1}{2}\%$	$116\frac{2}{3}\%$	1000%	$133\frac{1}{3}\%$
3.	3.50, $3\frac{1}{2}$	2.00, 2	3.45, $3\frac{9}{20}$	1.375, $1\frac{3}{8}$	2.60, $2\frac{3}{5}$	1.60, $1\frac{3}{5}$	7.05, $7\frac{1}{20}$
4.	1.75, $1\frac{3}{4}$	1.40, $1\frac{2}{5}$	6.00, 6	4.25, $4\frac{1}{4}$	1.15, $1\frac{3}{20}$	3.90, $3\frac{9}{10}$	$2.66\frac{2}{3}$, $2\frac{2}{3}$

89. Inventory Test

	a	b	c
1.	32	75%	256
2.	27	36	27
3.	100	10.1	2%
4.	64%	$133\frac{1}{3}$%	40

Page 116   89A. Practice Set   89B. Practice Set   Keeping Pace

89A	a	b	c	89B	a	b	c	KP			
1.	80	$33\frac{1}{3}$%	175	1.	400	460	21	1.	6.671	6.	51
2.	300	200	5%	2.	80%	144	$7\frac{1}{2}$%	2.	.265	7.	210
3.	75%	165	216	3.	50	80	200	3.	$9\frac{3}{4}$	8.	70%
4.	45	24	25%	4.	120	105	30	4.	$2\frac{3}{20}$	9.	20%
5.	18	72	64	5.	24	75%	$44\frac{4}{9}$%	5.	4.3	10.	150

Page 117   Applications

1. $4.00   2. $2.00   3. $160.00   4. $804.00   5. 1400 milligrams

6. 20 milligrams   7. 1400 milligrams   8. 18 milligrams   9. 25 gallons   10. 2800 gallons

Pages 118-20   Review of Applications: Ratio and Per Cent

1.	d	2.	b	3.	c	4.	c	5.	a	6.	a
7.	c	8.	b	9.	c	10.	c	11.	b	12.	d
13.	a	14.	c	15.	d	16.	b	17.	b	18.	b
19.	c	20.	c	21.	a	22.	b	23.	d	24.	b
25.	c	26.	a	27.	b	28.	d	29.	a	30.	c

Page 121   Review of Skills: Whole Numbers, Fractions, Decimals, and Per Cent

APPENDIX

Whole Numbers

1. 10	**2.** 20	**3.** 160	**4.** 260	**5.** 1860	**6.** 6260
7. 500	**8.** 900	**9.** 100	**10.** 6300	**11.** 8800	**12.** 4900
13. 2000	**14.** 2000	**15.** 1000	**16.** 13,000	**17.** 90,000	**18.** 65,000
19. c	**20.** a	**21.** b	**22.** c	**23.** a	**24.** a
25. b	**26.** b	**27.** a	**28.** a	**29.** b	**30.** a
31. c	**32.** d	**33.** b	**34.** b	**35.** b	

Page 125   Fractions

1. 1	**2.** 0	**3.** 1	**4.** 0	**5.** 1
6. 1	**7.** 2	**8.** 6	**9.** 31	**10.** 2
11. 20	**12.** 4	**13.** b	**14.** c	**15.** c
16. b	**17.** c	**18.** a	**19.** a	

Page 126   Decimals

1. 2	**2.** 26	**3.** 18	**4.** 17	**5.** 1	**6.** 9
7. 4.2	**8.** 4.7	**9.** 1.8	**10.** 7.1	**11.** .1	**12.** 8.5
13. 1.73	**14.** 2.47	**15.** 3.07	**16.** 8.03	**17.** .07	**18.** .01
19. .123	**20.** 1.803	**21.** .277	**22.** 7.005	**23.** .072	**24.** .001
25. a	**26.** b	**27.** a	**28.** a	**29.** c	**30.** b

Page 127   Per Cent

1. c	**2.** a	**3.** c	**4.** a	**5.** c	**6.** a
7. b	**8.** c	**9.** d	**10.** c		

Metric System -- Units of Length

1. a	**2.** b	**3.** c	**4.** b
5. Multiply by 1000	**6.** Divide by 100	**7.** Divide by 10	**8.** Multiply by 100
9. Multiply by 10	**10.** a	**11.** d	**12.** d
13. b	**14.** c		

Page 129   Metric System -- Units of Mass

1. c	**2.** c	**3.** b	**4.** a	**5.** a	**6.** d
7. b	**8.** a	**9.** a	**10.** b	**11.** a	**12.** b
13. b	**14.** b	**15.** d			

Page 130   Metric System -- Units of Capacity

1. a	**2.** b	**3.** c	**4.** a	**5.** b	**6.** b
7. c	**8.** d	**9.** a	**10.** c	**11.** 50	**12.** 3
13. 34	**14.** 4				

U.S. Measures -- Addition

1. 6 feet 3 inches
2. 6 feet 3 inches
3. 9 feet 6 inches
4. 8 yards 1 foot
5. 16 yards 1 foot
6. 10 yards
7. 12 yards 5 inches
8. 8 yards 21 inches
9. 8 yards 2 inches
10. 8 gallons 2 quarts
11. 13 gallons 1 quart
12. 70 gallons
13. 51 pounds 1 ounce
14. 17 pounds 4 ounces
15. 196 pounds 5 ounces
16. 14 hours 4 minutes
17. 10 hours 30 minutes
18. 31 hours 5 minutes
19. 9 weeks
20. 12 weeks
21. 6 weeks 4 days

U.S. Measures -- Subtraction

1. 1 foot 1 inch
2. 3 feet 3 inches
3. 10 feet 4 inches
4. 1 foot 4 inches
5. 3 feet 10 inches
6. 1 foot 6 inches
7. 3 yards 2 feet
8. 2 yards 2 feet
9. 2 feet
10. 1 gallon 1 quart
11. 2 gallons 1 quart
12. 2 gallons 2 quarts
13. 2 gallons 1 quart
14. 1 gallon 2 quarts
15. 4 gallons 2 quarts
16. 7 pounds 12 ounces
17. 1 pound 7 ounces
18. 171 pounds 2 ounces
19. 2 pounds 15 ounces
20. 2 pounds 14 ounces
21. 2 pounds 15 ounces
22. 2 hours 32 minutes
23. 3 hours 30 minutes
24. 3 hours 30 minutes
25. 3 days 22 hours
26. 2 days 23 hours
27. 2 days 21 hours

U.S. Measure -- Multiplication and Division

1. 11 feet 8 inches
2. 3 feet 6 inches
3. 21 feet 4 inches
4. 25 yards 2 feet
5. 58 yards 1 foot
6. 60 yards
7. 3 gallons 3 quarts
8. 58 gallons 2 quarts
9. 46 gallons
10. 22 hours 20 minutes
11. 31 hours 12 minutes
12. 74 hours
13. 1 yard 1 foot
14. 1 foot
15. 1 yard 1 foot
16. 4 gallons 1 quart
17. 6 gallons 1 quart
18. 3 quarts
19. 5 pounds 7 ounces
20. 5 pounds 8 ounces
21. 1 pound 14 ounces
22. 4 days 2 hours
23. 3 days 1 hour
24. 3 days 2 hours

SAMPLE COMPETENCY TEST

1. c
2. a
3. c
4. b
5. b
6. c
7. d
8. c
9. b
10. d
11. c
12. a
13. d
14. a
15. d
16. a
17. b
18. c
19. d
20. a
21. d
22. b
23. b
24. c
25. d
26. a
27. d
28. d
29. c
30. d
31. a
32. b
33. c
34. a
35. d
36. c
37. a
38. b
39. b
40. c
41. a
42. c
43. b
44. d
45. a
46. d
47. b
48. b
49. c
50. a